MW00657002

THANKFUL THURSDAYS:

25 Essays Expressing Gratitude for Science and Covering Other Fun Topics

Nicholas Kartsonis

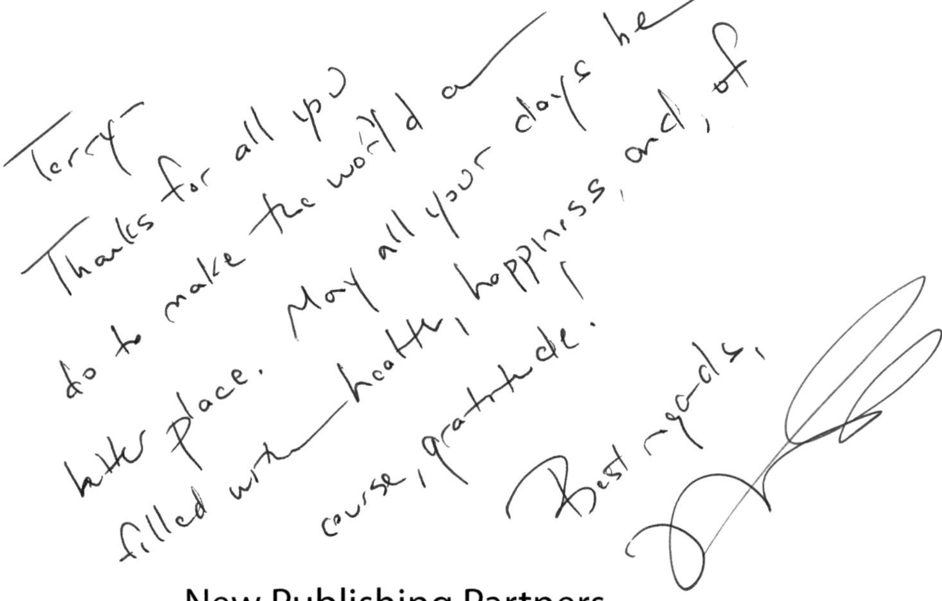
Terry—
Thanks for all you
do to make the world a
better place. May all your days be
filled with health, happiness, and, of
course, gratitude!
Best regards,

New Publishing Partners
Washington, DC

Published by New Publishing Partners
2510 Virginia Avenue
Suite 902N
Washington, DC 20037
www.npp-publishing.com

ISBN: 978-0-9882500-7-9

Cover design by Nicholas Kartsonis
Text and photo editing by Deborah Lange

Dedicated to the four individuals for whom I'm most thankful:
my endearing life partner, Daisy,
and our three talented sons—Chris, Sam, and Jack

Contents

Forward by Kenneth C. Frazier

I'd like to say Doctor Kartsonis is a Renaissance man. I'd like to, but I can't. Yes, of course, Nick is a scientist, a doctor, and an amateur historian. Nick's a man who delights in exploring the highways and byways of our scientific journey, especially if they happen to wind through the Garden State or end in my hometown of Philly. But no one with his execrable taste in music, somehow preferring Rush, Katy Perry, or Midnight Oil to Miles Davis, can truly be a Renaissance man. So, let's settle on polymath.

This collection of essays covers an extraordinary range of subjects across science, medicine, and history, with wide-ranging diversions into popular culture. I can guarantee you will learn something; you may even smile.

The origins of these essays show the essence of the author. Conceived as a way to display more kindness, have more fun, and show more gratitude, Nick has been building quite the fan club by entertaining his Merck colleagues with these tales every Thursday for a year, running up to the centenary of the birth of Dr. Maurice Hilleman.

Nick is an optimist. He believes in a better world. So, his big theme is gratitude, especially for those who have made a contribution. The real hero here is science. This book contains one of my favorite sentences, uttered by Tommy Francis and Jonas Salk, when announcing the result of the Polio vaccine trial, "the vaccine works. It is safe, effective, and potent."[1] What an inspiration to us all.

Here you can read the story of the Merck giant, Maurice Hilleman, the man who saved more lives in the twentieth century than any other, yet few today know his name. And Nick brings to life the achievements of many other extraordinary people you may never have heard of, such as Betty Bumpers and Dr. Elizabeth Blackwell.

The cast of characters you will meet along the way is extraordinary. From Hilleman, the vaccinologist, to Hamilton, both the founding father and the musical. Socrates to Sinatra. From Martin Luther King Jr. to Queen Elizabeth II. Alexander Graham Bell to Franklin Delano Roosevelt. As well as some of the most important molecules of our time— please take a bow, V920, MK-8591, and pembrolizumab.

---

1 Per the press release from April 12, 1955 from the Univerity of Michigan Information & News Service: "The First Press Release on Polio Vaccine Evaluation Results"

Isaac Newton, Nick reminds us, saw kindness as the act of building more bridges, not walls. Nick is a good man, a great colleague, and an extraordinary builder of bridges.

Kenneth C. Frazier
President, Chairman, and Chief Executive Officer, Merck & Co., Inc.

Introduction

Growing up as the child of Greek immigrants, I learned two tenets at an early age: (1) Never forget your roots; and (2) Never forget that an education is the equalizer across society.

Frankly, it's impossible for me to forget my roots. Being Greek is part of my essence. I am the proud first-generation product of devoted parents who emigrated to the United States from their impoverished lives in Southern Greece in the 1950-60s. Having spent my first ten years growing up on the Palisades in New Jersey, I took a city bus twice a week from my home town of Cliffside Park to the town of Fairview (down Anderson Avenue, for any of you familiar with Bergen County) to attend Greek School at the Ascension Greek Orthodox Church. While there, I learned to speak and write the Greek language and was indoctrinated into Greek Orthodoxy. Not surprisingly, I learned to speak Greek before I could speak English—as you might imagine, kindergarten was a bit of an overwhelming experience for me.

My Greekness was everywhere around me. Our simple, middle-class home was adorned with Greek statues of Athena and Zeus, and our living room was a shrine to the Acropolis. Dinner was always some version of a Greek delicacy. Basically, our primary concept of "meat and cheese" was lamb and Feta. In fact, I didn't have my first taste of peanut butter, a food foreign to Greek cuisine, until I had a peanut-butter cookie when I was 14 years old—fortunately, I was not allergic (I had been desensitized to nuts from my repeated exposure to baklava). My devoted aunt and uncle, who were essentially my second set of parents, lived in the house directly behind ours, and my revered grandmother (my "Yia Yia') resided in our basement. My other uncle and his lovely family lived only a few blocks away—well within walking distance. In essence, I had seven parents, and I knew it—especially when I was the subject of their admonishments after I was caught tramping in their beloved vegetable gardens in search of my missing Whiffle ball.

Even if I wanted to, I could not escape my Hellenistic roots. I learned early in life from my parents—all seven of them—my extended family, and my Greek school teacher, who had the classic name Aphrodite, that the most glorious time in history was, without dispute, The Golden Age of Greece. I was reminded on a near-daily basis that all the wonders of humanity—democracy, philosophy, the arts, and, of course, medicine—were the by-products of Athens and the other Greek city-states that ruled the world in fifth century BC. I was indoctrinated into the belief that stalwarts such as Pericles, Socrates, Sophocles, Aristophanes, and Hippocrates created civilized society, and, as their direct descendants, we should be forever thankful for the gifts these masterful Greek ancestors bestowed upon us. Naturally, I became captivated by the history of Greece, and, in turn, the history of mankind.

Early in life, I also learned that education helps flatten a hierarchical society. I quickly realized that manual, back-breaking labor was an inevitability that humans had to pay for the foibles of our predecessors. Half-jokingly, my dad declared that the unfortunate tribulations in one's life, that is, hard work, were a direct consequence of the Original Sin committed by Adam and Eve: "A life of hard work was all that emanated from the Garden of Eden." So, if you were a Greek immigrant, you either worked ungodly hours as the owner of a diner, or you operated a dry-cleaning shop. My father owned a dry-cleaning store on St. Nicholas Avenue in Washington Heights, just a stone's throw from the George Washington Bridge. I don't have many memories of being a preschooler, but I can vividly recall walking across that famous bridge with my mother and older brother, Phil, to visit my dad at his store. Unfortunately, one evening, my father's business was razed when an adjacent store fell victim to arson. Yet our family unit did not collapse. With all his grace and munificence, my uncle Demetrios (or Uncle "Jimmy," the one who lived a few blocks away), welcomed my father as a partner in his own dry-cleaning business, which was just a few blocks north on St. Nicholas Avenue. Both my father and my uncle worked incredibly long hours, often toiling in the sweltering heat each day from 6 AM to 6 PM. If you have ever spent any time on the premises of a dry-cleaning establishment where the mechanical steam pressers often reside, you're nodding your head right about now in violent agreement. A few years later, while closing up the shop one evening, my father was the victim of an attempted robbery, and, after an altercation with the armed robber, the villain fled—without the day's hard-earned money. However, the incident left an indelible mark in my father's mind, and a lasting scar where the bullet grazed his near-bald forehead. The event was enough to precipitate a change of locale.

My Uncle Jimmy settled his family in Jacksonville, Florida, where the Kartsonis family, led by my grandparents, had first emigrated to in the 1950s. My family would follow suit a few years' later. In Florida, both my father and uncle were the respected proprietors of their own dry-cleaning stores. I spent most afternoons and nearly every Saturday at my father's shop in the Arlington district of Jacksonville, where I perfected the artisan craft of *cash-register operator extraordinaire*. I became extremely facile at interacting with adults—a retail requisite for ensuring "impeccable customer service." My father would incessantly remind me that the way out of such a strenuous life was to excel in one's academic studies in elementary and secondary schools. He'd hold up as proof his own Jacksonville-based cousins, who had studied attentively to become physicians. In Greek, he would espouse the following: "Niko, if you want to be successful in life, you must always commit yourself to your studies. This is your chance to have a better life than I had."

So, I did as my dad suggested, and I studied hard—some might say, like a fiend.

I spent many days poring over books in the Floridian heat of the dry-cleaning enterprise, which somehow lacked air-conditioning! I would trudge through my Advanced Placement (AP) Chemistry, Biology, and Calculus homework on the same counter we used to sort customers' clothes. With a strong science and mathematics upbringing, I was well positioned to continue my studies in the STEM discipline.

Nonetheless, history remained my true love. I had an insatiable zest for American history, partly because it dovetailed well with the lessons I'd learned early in life about the history of my motherland, Greece. I also had an ardent appreciation for history because I adored my 11th grade American history teacher. At that time, Mrs. Frances Louise Smith Brewster was a 55-year old teacher who brought zeal and enthusiasm to her AP History curriculum. She had joined the Samuel W. Wolfson High School, a public school, in 1968, its inaugural year, which was the same year I was born. Already a widow of 17 years by the time I made her acquaintance, she dedicated her life to her classroom and its students. Referring to her students as her "cherubs," she taught the American Revolution, the Civil War, and the Industrial Revolution with a fervid passion. Although I can recall her recounting historical tales with emotion and vigor, I cannot recall her ever raising her voice or reprimanding the class. The worst we ever heard was: "Settle down, my sweet cherubs." And we would. She used to tell us how blessed she was to be a teacher and how she was always thankful each and every day to interact with such brilliant teenagers. One day, I went to see Mrs. Brewster after class, and I asked her how she was capable of maintaining her optimistic mindset. I'll never forget what she told me: "Although I lost my husband at any early age, I am thankful for every day I have on this Earth because I am blessed to teach the future leaders of the world. I try to remind myself of this point every day, and especially on Thursdays." When I inquired about the uniqueness of Thursday, Mrs. Brewster said with a wry smile: "It pairs well with Thankful, so it's only natural to exhibit extra thanks on this day. Oh, and by the way, it means there's only one more day after Thursday until the weekend."

After I graduated from Wolfson in 1986, I set off for college at Emory University in Decatur, just east of Atlanta. In addition to Ancient Greek 101, my first semester course load included an amazing course on the History of World War II in Europe. I recall coming home at winter break and informing my father about my burgeoning love for history after reading the ancient writings of the great Greek historian Herodotus. I confessed how I was seriously contemplating a major in History. With a stern look on his face, my father turned to me, and I'll never forget what he said, again in Greek: "Niko, nobody ever remembers the historians in the world. If you were to ask someone who Herodotus was, they would have no idea, but everybody knows Hippocrates. I'd suggest you become a doctor." A couple of years later, my family returned to New Jersey, as my father unfortunately suffered from allergic symptoms, including urticarial, from the dust mite that populated Northeast Florida. One Mother's Day in the late 1980s, I found myself back in New Jersey for the summer. That day, we attended services at the Holy Trinity Greek Orthodox Church in Westfield, New Jersey, where my Uncle Chris was one of the pastors. My aunt—the Presbytera (Greek for pastor's wife)—pointed out a grey-haired man at the front of the church who was there celebrating his own mother's selection as the Holy Trinity Parish's "Mother of the Year." My wonderful aunt said to me: "I think you should go meet that man: He's Dr. Roy Vagelos, the CEO at Merck." She introduced me to the delightful man, and I remember what Dr. Vagelos told me: "Becoming a physician is the most rewarding profession in the world. I've never regretted my decision, and you won't either."

So, I did what my dad and Dr. Vagelos suggested, and I became a physician.

While attending medical school at Emory in Atlanta, I quickly learned that life as a doctor might be rewarding, but it sure wasn't easy. In 1993, the Internal Medicine floors within Atlanta's gargantuan public hospital, Grady Memorial Hospital, were filled with young patients, most in their third or fourth decade of life, dying of AIDS. I can still recall ward after ward of gravely ill, skeleton-thin patients near death—and there was nothing I could do about it. I remember thinking to myself that becoming a physician was not as glorious as I thought it would be. I decided at that moment that I wanted to be a positive influence for better treatment options for these patients. So, it seemed only natural that after my Internal Medicine residency and an Infectious Disease fellowship in Boston, that I join Merck & Co., Inc.,[2] to help develop novel anti-infective drugs for these and other patients with infectious ailments. I did so at the suggestion of a former colleague of mine, Mike Severino, who had joined the company office outside of Philadelphia just a year or so earlier.

At Merck, I've been fortunate to be involved in the clinical development of a broad array of novel anti-infective agents—everything from antifungals to antibacterials, antivirals (including HIV medications) to vaccines, and small molecules to biologics. Some of these medicines have garnered regulatory licensure, and, in turn, I've witnessed a betterment of human health for many patients. At the same time, I've liaised with some of the greatest scientists of our era, ultimately gleaning an enormous amount of knowledge and wisdom from these individuals. Over my nearly two decades at Merck, I've been given the remarkable opportunity of assuming increasingly challenging roles within the company. In my current role, I provide oversight to both the Infectious Diseases and Vaccines disciplines in our Clinical Research department within the division of Merck Research Laboratories. Basically, I have a fulfilling career for which I am most thankful.

But how does one effectively demonstrate his appreciation and gratitude for having such a rewarding role?

I started earnestly wondering about this question in the months leading up to my 50th birthday. Prior to my birthday, March 3, 2018,

---

2 Merck & Co., Inc. is the official name for the company in the United States and Canada. Outside of these territories, the Company is formally known as Merck Sharp & Dohme (MSD). Going forward, in this book, I'll refer to the Company simply as Merck for the sake of convenience.

I had an existential moment when I asked myself what I was going to do differently in the second five decades of my life. After thinking about it for a few months and consulting with my wise partner Daisy, I convinced myself that I was going to cease three bad habits: quit worrying, avoid feeling guilty, and stop having regrets. I also told myself that I was going to accentuate three behaviors: display more kindness, have more fun, and show more gratitude.

In following up on this promise, I introduced a new workplace initiative in August 2018 that fulfilled the last item on my list—gratitude. This new initiative, called *Thankful Thursdays*, was inspired by the memory of Mrs. Brewster, who passed away at the age of 80 nearly a decade ago. *Thankful Thursday* was my humble attempt to write a weekly essay for my office teams expressing something for which I was thankful. In the spirit of fulfilling my two other focused areas for improvement, I intended these blogs to be a way to demonstrate kindness and empathy for all the incredible work our teams at Merck do, especially in the Infectious Disease and Vaccine area. I tried to also mix in some lighthearted humor and, of course, some lessons from history. In essence, this was also my one chance to fulfill my lifelong wish to become a historian.

I found myself writing most of these blogs on a Saturday morning, while my family slept in. I would then issue these *Thankful Thursday* notes via email every Thursday at exactly 6:00 AM between August 23, 2018 and August 30, 2019. My intent was to give my readers the opportunity to view something first thing every Thursday morning that was inspirational, educational, and, perhaps, a bit entertaining. In total, I wrote 48 essays during that 53-week span—even I needed some diastole (see my essay on this topic for further details). My primary intent was to share the email with my immediate team, but much like a highly contagious infectious pathogen, the project spread uncontrollably. Numerous individuals across the organization learned of my endeavor, and they joined the long, growing list of recipients of these Thursday morning emails. Over the year, I received accolades from my colleagues, with many of them encouraging me to make these essays available to the greater public in an effort to depict the awesome place where we work. That is, it was an opportunity to recite the true story of Merck and the joy of scientific discovery.

So, here we are.

For this book, I've selected 25 essays that I anticipate will resonate best with the broader community. I opted to include topics that touch on themes that might be relevant to a non-medical as well as medical community. For the most part, I've avoided including essays lauding particular products within the Merck portfolio, with a few exceptions, in an effort to avoid appearing promotional. I've also included the date of each essay, so you can appreciate the association of each essay to a particular date or event. Not all my essays are focused on the workplace. Along the way, I satisfied some of my own desires by heaping praise on persons, places, and events that have moved me in my life. Folks like Socrates and Nick Foles are rightfully recognized, as are wondrous places like Australia and New Jersey. That's right, I said New Jersey! For all you Jersey haters out there, if you take the time to read my essay on the marvelous Garden State, I think you'll appreciate that the small state nestled between New York and Pennsylvania is a treasured jewel.

In the spirit of the book's theme, I'd like to express my gratitude to you for purchasing and reading this collection of essays. I have no desire to profit from my work—the weekly catharsis I've experienced from crafting these stories is sufficient compensation for me. Thus, I plan to donate all the proceeds from the sale of this book to those who are in need. In the spirit of "paying it forward," I've chosen to divvy out any profits I receive in the first year to three worthy organizations that are striving to change the world. These are (1) Feeding America, a non-profit, domestic network of food banks dedicated to hunger relief in American cities; (2) St. Basil Academy, an orphanage and children's home in Garrison, New York that has long been affiliated with the Greek Orthodox Archdiocese of America; and (3) UNICEF, the division of the United Nations dedicated to developing community-level services to promote the health and well-being of the world's poorest children. Thereafter, I'll crowdsource to identify the best organizations to receive the earnings.

Let me close by also acknowledging the enormous elephant in the room. In today's world, I'll humbly admit that anything coming from the mouth of a pharmaceutical vice president might be viewed with a hefty dose of skepticism. In a world where branded and some generic medicines can often lack affordability, it's not unexpected or surprising that many patients, prescribers, and payers naturally question the business model, the methodology behind drug pricing, and the motive of the pharmaceutical industry as a whole. My book of essays is not intended to stir a debate about the relative cost of pharmaceuticals or healthcare in general. Nor is it intended to awaken a sleeping dragon, namely those fervent critics of the pharmaceutical industry. Instead, my intent is to illustrate to the world that that the scientists, engineers, and professionals who are employed in the pharmaceutical industry do noble and admirable research that helps advance science. My colleagues at Merck and other reputable pharmaceutical companies want what you want—better modern medicines to tackle cancer, heart failure, diabetes, and resistant bacterial organisms. In other words, we're all on the side of promoting the wellbeing of humanity. In the end, I hope my book gives you a more nuanced appreciation of this point. If I've failed in my pursuit, I hope you won't fault me for trying.

I sincerely hope you enjoy reading my selection of essays.

Essays

1 A Compelling Commitment to Combat a Compounding Crisis *(August 30, 2018)*

For this week's *Thankful Thursday* segment, I'm grateful for society's continued commitment to antibacterial research. As scientists, we develop new antibiotics because we realize that our existing anti-infective agents have a finite lifespan. As the average lifespan for a bacterium is only 12 hours, a microorganism will rapidly divide and evolve over time, especially in the face of stress. The unfortunate reality remains that antimicrobial resistance to our current antibacterial armamentarium is on the rise at an alarming rate, with new resistance mechanisms uncovered each year. Our collective development of novel anti-infectives must be an iterative process because any new agent will eventually lose its efficacy due to the organism's rapid adaptation. In other words, eventually all of our antibiotics—those miraculous discoveries of the twentieth century—will be lost forever to future generations.

To put this into its proper perspective, I thought I'd step back and tell you an intriguing tale about the disappearance of another of the world's great wonders.

Almost exactly 107 years ago, a little-known, underappreciated Renaissance masterpiece disappeared. On the early morning of Monday, August 21, 1911, three petty criminals walked out of the main entrance of the Louvre Museum in Paris with a blanket securely tucked under their arms. As it was just another manic Monday in Paris, no one paid much attention to what might be hidden under the blanket. As it turns out, the blanket concealed a small wooden canvas of a 400-year old painting originally known as *La Gioconda*—a 30 inch by 21 inch portrait of a Florentine silk merchant's wife, Lisa Gherardini del Giocondo. These three Italian handymen had visited the Louvre the day before, dressed in the traditional white smocks worn at that time by all museum employees. After puttering around for a few hours in the Louvre, they slipped into an art-supply closet. After the museum closed its doors to its patrons and all employees scurried home, the trio slipped out of their hiding place and moved over to the Renaissance gallery where *La Gioconda* was on display. They then lifted the 200 pounds of frame, painting, and protected glass and eventually made their way to the Louvre entrance at around daybreak, with the painting shrouded within a blanket. In a somewhat nonchalant manner, they walked to the Quai d'Orsay station, where they brazenly boarded an express train leaving the French capital. No one bothered to pay them attention. In fact, no one on the Louvre staff was even alarmed the next morning. At that time, paintings were routinely being moved from the gallery to the roof, where they were being photographed for a specific museum project.

Why the roof? Well, at the time, photography was still in its nascent stages. Camera shots were routinely performed outdoors in direct sunlight to enhance the contrasts.

A pushy local artist named Louis Beroud, who had traveled to the Louvre to paint the Renaissance gallery where *La Gioconda* hung among many other renowned works of art, was a bit perturbed that his painting was incomplete. So, Beroud asked the staff to go up to the roof to ascertain when the photographers would be returning *La Gioconda* to its rightful place on the gallery wall. Well, after what I envision was some bickering and a hearty eye roll, the staff member relented and trudged up the stairs to the roof. A few minutes later, he frantically raced down the stairs informing Beroud and any Louvre staff within earshot that the photographers had no idea where the painting was. *La Gioconda* had vanished.

The greatest art heist in history was rapidly unfolding. The Louvre closed its doors for a week while an investigation commenced. For nearly two and a half years, over 60 French detectives scoured the city, questioned suspects, and tried desperately to trace the steps of these criminals who dared to steal a Louvre treasure. Everyone was a suspect; in fact, the French poet Guillaume Apollinaire, the renowned artist Pablo Picasso, and the American tycoon J.P. Morgan were among the many famous art lovers questioned by these detectives. Unbeknownst to the French police, the real thieves were two brothers, Vincenzo and Michele Lancelotti, and their ring leader Vincenzo Perugia. These three men had stolen the masterpiece with the naïve intent of selling it on the black market. However, the media circus surrounding the crime had made the immediate sale an impossibility, so the painting remained hidden in Perugia's small Parisian flat for nearly 28 months. In November 2013, after the attention had died down to some extent, Perugia tried to sell the portrait to a Florentine art dealer in his native Italy. Fortunately, the art dealer knew that the painting was a smuggled treasure—one that ironically had been painted in the town of Florence nearly four centuries earlier. The shrewd art dealer convinced Perugia to leave the painting in his possession so he could have it fittingly appraised. Within hours, the police were alerted by the art dealer and Perugia was arrested. After a short stint at the Uffizi Museum in Florence, where thousands swarmed over a few weeks to see the masterpiece, *La Gioconda* was returned to the Louvre, where it resides to this day behind bullet-proof glass on the first floor in the Denon wing. You can go see it anytime.

Of course, *La Gioconda* is known to most of us affectionately as the *Mona Lisa*. As the renowned journalist John Lichfield once stated, Leonardo Da Vinci's magnum opus is the "best known, the most visited, the most written about, the most sung about, and the most parodied work of art in the world." Ironically, before its notorious theft, the painting was not well known outside of the art intelligentsia. The heist catapulted this little-known portrait into the global limelight. Prior to making its way to the Louvre in the nineteenth century, the *Mona Lisa* resided in several inconspicuous corners of the Fontainebleau Palace, the Palace of Versailles, and even Napoleon's bedroom in Tuileries Palace. In contrast, ten million people now queue up each year to catch a tiny glimpse of this lovely brown-eyed madam with her regal pose and quirky smile.

We are in the midst of celebrating a monumental milestone for the *Mona Lisa* creator. The year 2019 will mark the 500th anniversary of the death of Leonardo da Vinci, who at the time of his passing was a member of the royal court of the French monarch, Francis I. Recently, I had the chance to read a phenomenal biography about the masterful Renaissance Man who created the *Mona Lisa*. The wonderful historian and storyteller Walter Isaacson has written a riveting, in-depth examination about the Italian polymath in his thought-provoking bestseller, *Leonardo da Vinci*. Born out of wedlock in the Tuscan town of Vinci, Leonardo never received the formal education that was traditionally granted to most wealthy Florentine merchant family members. His affluent father chose not to afford Leonardo the same amenities bestowed to the father's legitimate heirs. Instead, as a curious, artistically-talented teenager, he was apprenticed to a reputable local artist, Verrocchio, who mentored him in the fine arts of painting, drawing, and sculpting, as well as the technical skills of plaster casting, metallurgy, and carpentry. Soon Leonardo was impressing his elder adviser with his beautiful, real-life portrayals on canvas, his meticulous attention to detail, and his relentless pursuit of perfection.

Ironically, in his lifetime, Leonardo was not prolific when it came to painting pictures; in fact, he is credited with creating fewer than 20 pieces of painted art, and many of these remained unfinished—at least in Leonardo's eyes. In fact, Leonardo continued to tweak many of his paintings until his death. Nevertheless, among his finished works, several are credited as the most famous art pieces in the history of the world. In addition to the *Mona Lisa*, his depiction of *The Last Supper*—the classic portrayal of Jesus's final repast with his 12 disciples—is regarded as a masterpiece of art in motion. Although his methodology in the use of shadows, depth perception, and motion are beyond the scope of this segment, I strongly encourage you to learn more about Leonardo's technique in Isaacson's biography. It will change your viewpoint as to how people lived, thought, and interacted half a millennium ago.

To put it bluntly, the impatient, left-handed Leonardo was never satisfied. He worked incessantly from day to night, creating beautiful works of art on canvas, mural, or sculpture, studying science including anatomy, physics, and astronomy, and drafting sketches. His copious journals of miniature drawings, sketches, and tracings are a glimpse into his racing mind. He studied geology, botany, and geography in excruciating detail. Like many before him, he even tried to square the circle, eventually resorting instead to creating his image of the perfect man within a circle (The Vitruvian Man). He even performed meticulous autopsies on cadavers—studying how the various organs in the human body work. In fact, his study of the physics of flowing rivers and his love of anatomy led him to hypothesize how the heart pumps blood and how this fluid eddies to close the valves within each chamber of the heart after each successive beat. He conceptualized flying machines that are analogous to helicopters, military weapons that are analogous to armored tanks, and entire towns that are analogous to modern-day cities with underground sewage systems. Basically, like Alexander Hamilton, another neglected polymath, Leonardo was simply non-stop. I like to believe that Leonardo and Hamilton shared the notion that they were running out of time and desperately needed to get all their ideas, thoughts, and aspirations down on paper. We'll circle back to Alexander Hamilton in a few weeks.

Today, we owe a debt of gratitude to Leonardo da Vinci. In his lifetime, he created masterpieces that have helped revolutionize our study of fine arts, architecture, and science. How would it feel if his works of art were truly lost forever?

Similarly, how would we feel if the great works of antibiotic development over the last 80 years were also lost forever?

As many of you are aware, the discovery and development of a new antibacterial agent is not for the faint at heart. Although the world has seen incredible advancement in antimicrobial agents since the discovery of penicillin and the sulfa antibiotics over eight decades ago, there really have been few antibacterial drugs with novel mechanisms of action in the last three decades; unfortunately, many of the low-hanging fruit were picked nearly four to five decades ago. Moreover, antibacterials are unique in the sense that their development is laborious, expensive, and extremely complex; the pricing model is not highly attractive; and most newly approved agents are placed in high reserve as an appropriate stewardship measure, in an effort to avoid resistance from overuse. To put it bluntly, antibacterials are not blockbusters for the pharmaceutical industry. Ironically, the problem is compounded by the fact that the development of novel antibacterials needs to iterative, as all new agents will eventually lose their efficacy due to the organism's rapid adaptation and eventual drug resistance. So, it should really not come as a surprise that many pharmaceutical companies have left this field in the last decade. The mass exodus has increased in the last few years, as large companies like AstraZeneca, Novartis, and Sanofi have abandoned their antibacterial discovery programs.

Yet, the unfortunate reality is that antimicrobial resistance is on the rise, with new resistance mechanisms identified in the last few decades that hinder our use of what have historically been our agents of last resort, such as the carbapenem class of β-lactams. We have resorted to using older agents, such as colistin, which have suboptimal efficacy and notable safety concerns. Epidemiologists estimate that if we do not change the trajectory we are currently on regarding novel antibacterial development, antimicrobial resistance will have massive public health implications. Some experts, like the British economist Jim O'Neill, even go so far as to predict that by 2050, ten million people will die annually as a result of resistance to diseases like bacterial infections, malaria, tuberculosis, and HIV, unless a global response to the problem is mounted.

All this creates a potential perfect storm that impacts our own lives and the lives of future generations.

So today, I'm grateful that Merck has seen antibacterial discovery and development as a core mission, and our corporate predecessors have not wavered in this mission since the launch of our company's first antibiotic in 1939. Over the last eight decades, Merck and its affiliates have been instrumental in bringing many new antibacterial agents to the market (my last count puts the number at 15). The list includes crucial agents that have changed the course of medicine: sulfamerazine (1939), penicillin (1941), streptomycin (1945), cefoxitin (1979), imipenem (1983), and ertapenem (2001), just to name a few (see **Figure 1** to learn about a married couple who were instrumental in several of these advances). Even today, we are working to advance the core development of novel investigational agents, such as imipenem/cilastatin/relebactam and ceftolozane/tazobactam. On top of this, our Discovery group continues to work tirelessly to identify newer targets that will hopefully tackle pathogens that are not covered by our current portfolio and eventually address the resistance that will inevitably develop to those agents in our current repertoire. I'm thankful for our commitment to this critical space and to the researchers and scientists across all our Merck development teams who have remained steadfast in fulfilling this important mission. Finally, I'm appreciative of all the other pharmaceutical companies and research entities that have chosen to invest in this field. Their dedication and commitment to the task at hand should not go unnoticed.

One thing is paramount in my mind: I don't want to live in a post-antibiotic era. Sadly, we sometimes don't miss a masterpiece until it is no longer with us. I can promise you that we will invariably miss our antibiotics—our marvels of the twentieth century—when they're long gone, just like the world missed Leonardo's sixteenth century painting of the *Mona Lisa* after it vanished from the Louvre in 1911. Great works created by innovative giants, regardless of origin—whether from an Italian Renaissance artist or a Merck chemist—should not only be treasured but properly preserved. In turn, it's our mission to follow in the footsteps of these venerable giants, as we venture forward to change the world.

2 Mindful of My Magnificent Microbiome *(September 6, 2018)*

For this week's *Thankful Thursday* segment, I offer up my gratitude and pay homage to my good friend—my microbiome. The medical innovation that might one day come from the study of all the different microorganisms that live within our own bodies is something that greatly excites me about the future of medicine. Although we have only just begun to scratch the surface of our understanding of the microbiome and its potential interplay on various medical conditions, microbiome research is an untapped reservoir for future drug development.

Unfortunately, we are not there yet. Are you willing to wait for it?

Philosophers say patience is a virtue, and I think it is true for the most part. As the great Russian author Leo Tolstoy, once quipped: "The two most powerful warriors are patience and time."[3] In our busy worlds where we have access to an endless slew of information at our proverbial fingertips—thanks to the discovery of the Internet and smart phone technology—it is often difficult for humans to have wait idly for anything. Most of us will do just about anything to avoid waiting in line, whether it is the Transportation Security Administration (TSA) line for security at an airport, for a dinner table at a fancy restaurant, or for the next ride at Disney World. Hence, we now have time-saving innovations such as TSA Precheck, Open Table, and Fast Pass. But, sometimes, you just can't bypass the line; that is, you simply must wait your turn for greatness to take hold.

3 Leo Tolstoy, source unknown.

I learned my share about this topic in a somewhat unusual way a summer ago. Back in July 2017, I was embarking on a short vacation for the Independence Day holiday in Martha's Vineyard with my lovely partner, Daisy. The lack of access to my computer left me, well, lying in wait. As we waited for the ferry to cross over to the Vineyard, Daisy encouraged me to listen to a musical she had been introduced to by our oldest son, Chris. I was not really in an artistic or melodic mood, but, since I was without a book to read or my usually trustworthy laptop to pass the time, I followed her advice and listened to the music from the award-winning Broadway production on my iPhone. Well, the music was awesome, and as our ferry approached the Vineyard, I had tears gushing down my face as I listened with my earbuds to the musical's finale, "Who Lives, Who Dies, Who Tells Your Story." I was so blown away by the story that I immediately yearned to see the live production. A few months and a few hundred dollars later, Daisy, members of our family, and I were off to the Richard Rogers Theater in New York City. The show was well worth the wait—and the exorbitant price of admission.

Of course, the musical I'm cagily referring to is *Hamilton*—a nearly three-hour, non-stop story of the determined immigrant Alexander Hamilton and his endless pursuit of freedom, prosperity, and legacy. If you have never listened to the music from *Hamilton* or seen the production on Broadway or on tour, you simply are missing out. Irrespective of the type of music you like, I can promise you that *Hamilton* will keep you thoroughly entertained. The musical is the masterful brainchild of Lin-Manuel Miranda, an incredible, forward-thinking artist who had prior to *Hamilton's* production already earned his share of fame and recognition for his Tony Award-winning musical *In the Heights*. Based on Ron Chernow's comprehensive, well-researched biography of the first United States Secretary of the Treasury, Hamilton has been described as the quintessential artistic masterpiece. The production is a veritable magnum opus that artistically blends an awesome story of the least-known founding father with an eclectic variety of musical genres—including musical show tunes, English love ballads, rock, jazz, rhythm and blues tunes, and, of course, hip-hop and rap. If you don't want to take my word for it, take the word of the former First Lady, Michelle Obama: "It was simply, as I tell everybody, the best piece of art in any form that I have ever seen in my life."[4] She's not exaggerating. *Hamilton* is that good, and I can't wait until I see it again. In fact, I don't know why I waited so long to see it in the first place.

Hamilton gives me the opportunity to expound a bit about the natural tug-and-pull we face in our daily lives between the power of maintaining patience and waiting for something good to transpire versus the inevitable finality of time. Humans are naturally impulsive creatures; yet, we also excel at allowing our prior experiences to influence our future actions—in fact, the latter forms the basis of wisdom. The Hamilton story is all about the "yin yang" that humans face between the impulsive desire to "go for broke" vs. the more cautious, risk-averse approach for waiting for things to naturally run their course. In the Broadway musical, Alexander Hamilton is a prototype of the former, while Aaron Burr, his friend-turned-rival, is an exemplar of the latter. The opening numbers in the musical demonstrate exactly why Hamilton is such a braggadocious, carefree whipper-snapper. As an abandoned orphan, Hamilton was graced by the generosity of others who paid for his travels from the Caribbean to New York City after realizing his extraordinary potential as an author. Hamilton learned at any early age that if he was going to be successful in life, he was not going to have it bestowed upon him. In short, he would not "throw away his shot" but rather go after whatever he wanted. As he proclaims so eloquently in one of my favorite songs, the rap ditty, "My Shot!":

"I'm past patiently waiting, I'm passionately mashing every expectation. Every action's an act of creation. I'm laughing in the face of casualties and sorrow. For the first time, I'm thinking past tomorrow."

With his raison d'etre fully reaffirmed, Hamilton stands up for what he believes in and goes after what he wants—fighting valiantly in the American Revolution in an all-out pursuit of American independence; taking on a challenging new role as Washington's war-time secretary/strategist at the General's behest; eagerly accepting and excelling at the Secretary of Treasury post in President's Washington cabinet; and, of course, endlessly wooing the beautiful, well-to-do daughter of General Schuyler, Ms. Eliza. As a self-proclaimed zealot and massive

---

4 Reported in "Hamilton v Trump: visions for America from a Broadway show – and a showman" by David Smith in *The Guardian* on March 19, 2016.

pain, he pushes the envelope on more than one occasion, stepping on his share of toes. Of course, good things come to him in his impulsive pursuits...until they don't.

Meanwhile, his counterpart, Aaron Burr is slower to react. Espousing to the mindset of never letting "others know what you're against or what you're for," Burr takes a more methodical, calculated approach. As he notes in his response to several young revolutionaries in a tavern one night, "I see you're takin' a stand; you spit, I'm 'a sit, and we'll see where we land." We learn more about his deliberative, thoughtful approach later in the musical, in an aptly-named song, "Wait for It." So, as the years pass, Burr is glacially slow to support the American Revolution, the new US Constitution, and public service. When he finally decides to enter the political mix, his "stand on the sidelines and don't commit to anything" approach does not garner him the support of his once-beloved friend, Hamilton, or even the American public. A bit exasperated, Burr decides to finally take an impulsive approach against Hamilton, and, well, you know what happens next.

So, as I waited patiently for the ferry to arrive at Martha's Vineyard, I took advantage of the time away from the laptop to learn an important lesson. In the end, there's risk in both taking an impulsive, often-innovative approach and in waiting for things to play themselves out a bit more. The two contrasting styles within *Hamilton* speak volumes to the same turmoil we often face with technological advances. Sometimes they just need time for greatness to reveal itself.

In my humble estimation, science works in much the same way.

Probably the most popular and least understood concept in the world of microbiology today is the human microbiome. Astonishing as it may seem, it turns out that each one of us harbors around ten trillion to a hundred trillion symbiotic microbial cells in our bodies. Biologists estimate that there are more than ten thousand different microbe species, including bacteria, fungi, and viruses, that inhabit each and every one of us, in places like our oral cavity, gut, urogenital tract, skin, and bloodstream. These organisms have learned to live not only within our tissues but also with each other. Together, the human host and our microbiome have evolved as a synergistic unit, ultimately relying on each other to maintain a sense of equilibrium and physical wellness.

It is probably too extensive for me to go through all the ways our microbiome assists us in our daily lives, but I thought it might be fun to highlight a few pretty cool examples:

For years, we've known that antibiotics can disrupt the normal gut microbiota, and this, in turn, could allow for certain bad pathogens, such as *Clostridium difficile* (or *C. diff*), to spread unchecked in the gut. This can result in a serious, debilitating diarrheal illness that can even lead to death. We now know that those individuals that fully recover from a first episode of the infection require a restoration of a diverse microbiota in their gut, or otherwise they are at risk of developing a recurrence of *C. diff*. The less diverse the regrowth of the microbiota, the higher the chance for a recurrence. One of the reasons I believe bezlotoxumab (Merck's monoclonal antibody against a key pathogenic toxin, Toxin B, produced by *C. diff*) is a viable option for patients with *C. diff* recurrence is that it has no effect on the existing microbiota, thereby allowing time for the human body to respond to the recent gut insult caused by the infection; in other words, by neutralizing any Toxin B that might result in clinical symptoms present in the gut from residual *C. diff* after an antibiotic course, bezlotoxumab affords the time for the body to restore the microbiome with healthy microorganisms.

The bacteria that live in the human gut also play an important role in our natural immune response or even our immune response to vaccines. Studies have shown that the higher the diversity in the gut microbiota, the broader one's natural response to infectious pathogens. Furthermore, the higher the diversity in the gut microbiota, the greater the magnitude of the body's immune response to certain vaccines. Clearly, this interplay is crucial to ensuring an optimal immune response to the vaccines we develop. In fact, scientists have begun examining the effect of the microbiome on vaccine responsiveness and durability in an effort to better understand this interaction and, hopefully, one day allow us to optimize the use of our current and future vaccine candidates.

Earlier this year, the journal *Science* published a really fascinating article on the importance of the microbiome, and specifically, microbial diversity in our gut, in impacting response of cancer patients to new immune-oncology therapies, such as immune checkpoint inhibitors (ICIs) pembrolizumab and nivolumab. Abnormal gut microbiome composition, especially after recent antibiotic use, can have a negative effect on ICIs. A less diverse microbiota at the time of treatment, especially one lacking certain microorganisms, increases the chance of therapeutic failure. Moreover, the researchers found that germ-free mice receiving fecal microbiota transplantations from cancer patients can actually replicate the finding seen in humans.

Pretty impressive stuff.

But, then, if this was not awesome enough, *The New York Times* published an absolutely wonderful article by Carl Zimmer on September 3, 2018, describing how the pharmaceutical industry can use the normal bacteria that take root in the microbiome to help us fight off certain diseases. The article highlights the ongoing work of a company called Synlogic, which is based in Boston and uses synthetic biology to fashion microbes that can then be imported into bodies and can treat us from within. In this case, the bacteria are designed to treat a rare inherited disease called phenylketonuria, or PKU. About 16,000 infants are born each year with some form of PKU. Individuals who inherit this condition cannot break down the amino acid phenylalanine; an excess of this amino acid can result in seizures, intellectual compromise, and mental disorders. It is, for this reason, patients with PKU must avoid dietary protein that is high in this amino acid, such as cheese, eggs, and lean meat, and even diet soft drinks. If you read the label on your next Diet Coke, you'll see what I mean! *The New York Times* article shows that the researchers at Synlogic have engineered *E. coli*, a common bacteria that normally lives in our guts, with certain genes that would contain the DNA for proteins that would (1) allow the excess influx of the amino acid into *E. coli* and (2) break down the amino acid. The *E. coli* turn on these genes only in oxygen-deficient conditions, such as exist in the intestines, so the bacteria only work once they enter the gut. The researchers showed in both mice and monkeys that the levels of phenylalanine could be controlled or reduced in those animals that ingested the engineered bacteria. Synlogic has now moved on to humans, where they have shown that ingestion of this engineered bacteria is safe in normal healthy volunteers. Phase 2 studies in patients with PKU are now commencing in an effort to demonstrate proof of concept in humans. How cool is this.

Frankly, if these examples do not fill you with a sense of awe, then perhaps you might need to consider a career change.

All kidding aside, our growing knowledge of the microbiome and the ability of discovery scientists to tap into this gold mine of research fills me with boundless enthusiasm, vigor, and hope. I'm so grateful for the wisdom we have gained on this topic over the last few decades, and I am excited about the possibilities this holds for human health in the future. It is no wonder that our leadership within Merck Research Laboratories have established a team in the Boston Discovery hub to better explore the role of the microbiome in helping us discover new agents to treat human disease in the future. My sincere appreciation goes out to all those who have worked on programs like bezlotoxumab, the group working on experimental studies assessing vaccine response in relation to microbiome diversity, and the scientists in Merck's Boston discovery hub who are on the cusp of discovery efforts in this area. I'm also thankful for those at Synlogic, other companies, and academic research institutions who are delving into this area. I eagerly await what the future holds in this field.

I predict that one day we'll all live in a world where when confronted with a difficult biomedical disease, we can turn and say, "No worries, mate. There's a bacterium for that."

I know this sounds a bit insane, but as Alexander Hamilton so enthusiastically tells us in the opening act of the musical bearing his name, "There are a million things I haven't done. Just you wait!" Even his lovely bride, Eliza Hamilton, eloquently sums it up in the final verse in the *Hamilton* musical, "It's only a matter of time."

3 A Belated Birthday Blog for a Brilliant Biologist *(September 14, 2018)*

For this week's *Thankful Thursday* segment, I want to take a moment and pass along my gratitude to Dr. Maurice Hilleman, a former Merck employee, who left behind an incredible legacy in the field of vaccinology. I also want to use this moment to thank all those who continue to enhance the legacy he pioneered more than half a century ago.

Do you know that horrible feeling of missing someone's birthday? You wake up one day, and, while you're brushing your teeth or working out on the elliptical, you say to yourself: "Oh @$&!*. I forgot my brother's birthday." Sadly, this happened to me just earlier this week. I woke up and realized that August 30 came and passed, and I forgot to pass along birthday wishes to a man I greatly admire. So, today, my segment is dedicated to offering up a belated birthday blessing to a brilliant biologist!

Indeed, August 30, 2018, would have been the 99th birthday of a man to whom the world owes an enormous debt of gratitude—the venerable Dr. Maurice Hillman (**Figure 2**). The co-founder and director of the Institute of Human Virology at the University of Maryland, Dr. Robert Gallo, described Maurice Hilleman as "the most successful vaccinologist in history." As Gallo so aptly states, the name "Hilleman" should be joined forever with other remarkable scientists, like Louis Pasteur and Robert Koch, "in the story of man's striving against pathogens."[5] Ironically, however, Hilleman rarely gets the credit he

5 Reported in "Maurice R. Hilleman, 85; Scientist Developed Many Vaccines

deserves. As the American political activist Ralph Nader so elegantly describes Hilleman's situation: "Almost no one knew about him, saw him on television, or read about him in newspapers or magazines. His anonymity, in comparison with Madonna, Michael Jackson, Jose Canseco, or an assortment of B-grade actors, tells something about our society's and media's concepts of celebrity—much less of the heroic."[6] To my dismay, Hilleman never received a Nobel Prize for any of the eight vaccines that we now routinely administer to the American youth. He was never publicly lauded for his role in delineating the etiology for a variety of microbial infections—chlamydia, adenovirus, and several of the viruses that cause hepatitis. The lessons he taught us about genetic "drifts" and "shifts" in certain viruses, especially influenza, were instrumental in defining a path to medically address such infections today. Yet, he was never publicly idolized for this insight or the countless number of lives he saved from the 1957 influenza pandemic. As Anthony Fauci, Director of the National Institute of Allergy and Infectious Diseases, so eloquently puts it: Hilleman's contribution was "the best kept secret among the lay public. If you look at the whole field of vaccinology, nobody was more influential."[7]

As we learned over the past weeks with the tales of Leonardo Da Vinci and Alexander Hamilton, sometimes our most prized heroes—the true polymaths who've walked this earth—are not fully appreciated for the legacy they leave behind. Their brilliant accomplishments are often not valued for generations or, worse yet, not recognized until one of their masterpieces or discoveries goes missing. How many of us have taken for granted our nation's financial and banking system, a work of sheer brilliance conceived by the first Secretary of the Treasury, Alexander Hamilton? Or the incredible beauty of the *Mona Lisa*, a magnum opus that was not fully appreciated until it was stolen from the Louvre? Or even the combination vaccine against measles, mumps, and rubella, Hilleman's masterful vaccine that has saved generations of children from the hardships of three different childhood diseases? As we stand witness to a rise in outbreaks of measles around the world due to lack of vaccination, we are only now beginning to truly

---

That Saved Millions of Lives" by Thomas H. Maugh II in the *Los Angeles Times* on April 13, 2005.

6 "Scientists or Celebrities?" by Ralph Nader in *CounterPunch* on April 16, 2005.

7 "Maurice Hilleman" by Laura Newman in the *British Medical Journal,* April 30, 2005.

appreciate the miraculous value of this medical innovation. As Lin-Manuel Miranda asked in the closing act of his tribute to Hamilton: "When they're gone, who'll remember their name? Who keeps their flame? Who tells their story?"

Well, the answer to these queries is simple: It's up to you and me to ensure the legacy of these pioneers is lasting and never forgotten. Maurice Hilleman's legacy warrants cementing, and today I plan to continue the noteworthy praise of this remarkable scientist.

As I think back on the life of Maurice Hilleman, I shudder to think what might have transpired if Hilleman had not grown into the preeminent leader he is certainly recognized to have become. Can you imagine what might have been if Hilleman had not survived his childhood a century ago? Sadly, neither Hilleman's mother nor his twin sister survived his birth that fateful day in the late August summer of 1919. Born into poverty amidst the Great Depression in the small farming town of Miles City, Montana, Hilleman and his seven older siblings were raised on a nearby farm by their caring uncle and aunt. Separated from his parents, Hilleman nearly died a second time at the age of 8, when he contracted a severe case of diphtheria. But not only did he survive that additional insult, he thrived. His fair share of childhood hardships and his troubling station in life never deterred him in his pursuit of a better existence. Despite repeated brushes with death, Hilleman marveled at the beauty of life and took immense pleasure in learning about nature by helping to rear the chickens and cattle on the farm, by perfecting the art of broom-making as part of his family's business, and by learning the subtle intricacies of science. He had a voracious appetite for science shows on the radio, and he also liked to build radios and other electrical devices by hand. He spent his spare time as a teenager attentively reading on topics such as chemistry, microbiology, and zoology—even choosing to read Charles Darwin's *Origin of Species* in an effort to better comprehend the concept of evolution, much to the disappointment and disapproval of his Lutheran minister. Not surprisingly, he was granted the high school award at his graduation for the most outstanding science student.

After graduating from the local public high school in Custer County in 1937, the 18-year old Hilleman desperately wanted to attend college, but his lack of any financial backing for a postgraduate education led him to accept a job at the local JC Penney's department store. After a year of working in retail, Hilleman was thrilled to discover

s that Montana State University, in the ng full merit scholarships for prospective d and received a full 4-year scholarship utifully double majored in microbiology er, after graduating as the valedictorian d in a doctoral graduate program in of Chicago, where he took an interest he, ironically enough, studied in lamydia was caused by a gram-negative overturn prior-held notions that ral infection. He completed a five-year d parasitology in just three years.

tion ended in 1944, Hilleman took ne Bristol-Myers Squibb), where he gainst Japanese B encephalitis— a caused by a zoonotic virus and that was extremely problematic for the US troops stationed in the Asia Pacific. While there, he also oversaw Squibb's vaccine programs for rabies and small pox. In 1948, he took a job at Walter Reed Institute of Research, where he spent the next decade studying the effect of respiratory viruses. While at Walter Reed, Hilleman helped develop the first vaccine against two key serotypes that caused adenovirus infection. He also took a strong interest in the virus that causes influenza.

During his early career, Dr. Hilleman observed that the influenza virus routinely changes over time. Sometimes the changes are small (drifts), but other times they can be dramatic (shifts). Antigenic shift can result in influenza pandemics because, when they occur, very few individuals in the world are immune to the significantly-changed virus.

One day in April 1957, while sitting in his office, Hilleman read a *New York Times* report of an aggressive influenza outbreak in Hong Kong, wherein ten percent of the population (250,000) had developed significant influenza disease. He suspected a pandemic on par with what was regrettably observed in 1918 might be brewing. So, the next day, he cabled the army's laboratory staff at the US base in Zama, Japan, and he ordered them to collect swabs of throat washings from any service member that was suffering from suspected influenza. Once he collected the samples, he analyzed them relative to banked samples in his laboratory. He discovered what we feared most. Only a handful of the banked samples displayed antibody against the virus (which turned out to be H2N2), and all of those were from individuals in their 70s and 80s who had survived the 1889-90 influenza pandemic. So, under Hilleman's direction, Merck and a few other pharmaceutical companies developed a vaccine that specifically targeted the 1957 strain. In fact, Merck provided the pilot batch of the vaccine that was tested at Walter Reed. Even without a government subsidy to mass produce the vaccine, Merck decided to mass produce the vaccine because if a pandemic were to occur, they wanted the US population to be prepared. Once they did receive the formal go from the government, Merck launched a crash program of unprecedented scale, ultimately producing three million doses a week, as Louis Galambos would state in his book *Networks of Innovation*. Together, Hilleman, Merck, and others created a vaccine before the virus could arrive later that year in the U.S. Merck delivered more influenza vaccine to the US stockpile that year than any other company—a total of 20 million doses (nearly half that provided by the entire industry). Although 70,000 deaths in the U.S. occurred as a result of the 1957 pandemic, public health officials estimate that the number of American deaths could have reached one million had Dr. Hilleman's vaccine not been available.

At that point, Hilleman could have probably hung up his cleats and called it a successful career. Fortunately, he chose to keep at it. Max Tishler, the Merck Research Laboratories head, and John Connor, Merck's CEO, were so impressed by Hilleman that in 1957 they offered him the job to lead Merck Vaccines Research. His decision to accept a job at Merck changed the course of history forever.

When Hilleman joined Merck, he was asked to head up the new virus and cell biology development department in West Point, Pennsylvania. He went on to develop the first measles vaccine by developing an attenuated version of the virus. The measles vaccine was subsequently released in 1963. Later, when his 5-year old daughter, Jeryl Lynn, developed mumps, he harvested the virus from her throat and drove it to Merck West Point facility in the middle of the night, ahead of a business trip he had planned that day, to ultimately develop the mumps vaccine. He went on to develop a vaccine for German measles (rubella) as well; when combined with the earlier two vaccines, the trivalent vaccine for measles, mumps, and rubella was born and was officially launched in 1971. We use essentially the same vaccine today, with some minor modifications, to vaccinate our children in the US and other parts of the world. But the legacy did not end there.

Hilleman would contribute to the development of vaccines for Hepatitis A, Hepatitis B, *S. pneumoniae, H. influenzae, N. meningitidis,* and chicken pox (Varicella). Hilleman retired from Merck in 1984 at the age of 65 years, as this was the mandatory retirement age at that time for all Merck employees. During his illustrious 27-year career, Hilleman would develop 8 of the 14 vaccines given to young infants and children in the developed world. In the Animal Health area, he played a crucial role in developing a vaccine against Marek Disease—a concerning cause of cancer in chickens. In total, Hilleman helped write over 450 publications and contributed to the development of more than 40 different vaccines for humans and animals. Most importantly, the vaccines he helped pioneer have saved countless lives. It's hard to estimate exactly how many lives are saved each year as a direct result of Hilleman's work, but one thing is for sure—the numbers are in the millions. Let me quote Anthony Fauci one more time for emphasis: "Just one of his accomplishments would be enough to have made for a great scientific career. One can say without hyperbole that Maurice changed the world with his extraordinary contributions."[8]

So, today, I am grateful for the medical scientist who saved more lives in the twentieth century than anyone else. Hilleman inspires me to be a better leader. I am also so appreciative of the legacy of pediatric vaccines that Hilleman helped to institute at Merck. Today, we contribute to this legacy through the great work the various development teams and their subteams undertake in supporting these pediatric vaccines. These teams continue to do stellar work to support the lifecycle management of these programs. We also continue the mission by exploring new pediatric vaccine targets to address *S. pneumoniae,* CMV, and dengue, to name a few troubling infectious pathogens.

So, with that, let's wish a Happy 99th birthday to the one and only, Dr. Maurice Hilleman! I might have forgotten your birthday, but I'll never forget all the incredible, life-saving gifts you gave us.

Your legacy will always be secure with your colleagues at Merck. We'll always be there to tell your story.

---

8 "Maurice Hilleman, Master in Creating Vaccines, Dies at 85" by Laurence K. Altman in *The New York Times*, April 12, 2005.

P.S. If you have never seen the documentary film on Dr. Hilleman's life, I suggest you do so. It is called *Hilleman: A Perilous Quest to Save the World's Children*. Dr. Paul Offit, a pediatrician from the Children's Hospital of Pennsylvania, has also written an inspiring book about Dr. Hilleman's life, entitled *Vaccinated: One Man's Quest to Defeat the World's Deadliest Diseases*.

4 The Power of Philanthropy *(November 9, 2018)*

For this week's *Thankful Thursday* segment, I want to share my gratitude and appreciation for all the philanthropists whose thoughtful humanitarian gifts have had a substantial impact on humanity.

On November 8, 1979, the retired chairman of the Coca-Cola Company, Robert W. Woodruff, gave, what was at that time, the single largest gift in the history of American philanthropy (**Figure 3**). Mr. Woodruff proffered $100 million to Emory University in the form of about three million shares of Coca-Cola Company stock. Combined with other donations he provided to the institution, Mr. Woodruff would ultimately give about $210 million to Emory over the course of his life. The most amazing aspect about this donation is that Mr. Woodruff never graduated from Emory. In fact, the school booted him out after attending only a single term; as Mr. Woodruff once put it, the only thing he ever excelled at Emory was "cutting classes and spending money." After dropping out of college, he started working as a laborer and then a machinist at a pipe and foundry company in Atlanta, where he learned the importance of having a strong work ethic. He eventually made his way into sales at an ice and coal company, and then a prosperous automobile company, before ultimately parlaying his way into becoming the president at Coca-Cola Inc. Under his leadership, Coca-Cola would grow into one of the largest publicly traded companies in the world. Mr. Woodruff was adept at promoting its premier soda product through its famous ad campaigns on television and radio: "Things Go Better with Coke," "It's the Real Thing," and "Have a Coke and a Smile." The last one listed here was always my favorite. Even more so, who doesn't fondly remember the famous Coke commercial with the injured Mean Joe Greene? Who wouldn't want to teach the world to sing in perfect harmony? Is there anything more entertaining than watching polar bears drink a Coke while marveling at the Aurora Borealis? OK I'll readily concede that last one was not under Woodruff's reign as CEO, but the visual still brings a smile to my face.

As Mr. Woodruff, then a nonagenarian, would admit to Emory students in the 1980s, the sheer shame he felt from being forced out of Emory was the impetus that ultimately catapulted him into becoming one of the most prosperous businessmen in the world. His benevolent gift to Emory was really a return of the award the college gave to him some 60 years earlier: the drive to succeed. The reason I'm recalling this story for this week's *Thankful Thursday* segment is that it was Mr. Woodruff's charitable generosity the would afford me the ability to attend Emory College and, eventually, the Emory School of Medicine. As Greek immigrants who owned a small dry-cleaning shop in Jacksonville, Florida, my parents lacked the financial resources to send me to Emory for my postgraduate education, which at the time was a whopping tuition of about $12 thousand per year; the scholarship foundation that Emory had set up with the monies provided by Mr. Woodruff afforded me the opportunity to attend Emory College in Atlanta starting in 1986, and then Emory University Medical School starting in 1990. I am forever grateful for the gift Emory gave me, and, indeed, this is the reason I always answer my cell phone when a 404 area code number appears. It is also the reason you see me drinking Diet Coke or Coke Zero only. Only when times are so dire that I would deign to drink a soda product from the Pepsi Company.

I chose this topic today because I continue to be amazed by the generous donations that I have seen in the last few years. I want to take a moment to acknowledge some of these incredible acts of benevolence, as they give me hope in a world that is routinely dominated by negative news.

Let's start with the generous donations afforded by Bill and Melinda Gates to their foundation, the Bill and Melinda Gates Foundation (BMGF). Launched in 2000, the BMGF is the largest private foundation in the US, with assets totaling over $50 billion. Operating under the mantra that "All Lives Have Equal Value," the BMGF focuses on ensuring that all of the world's citizens have access to quality healthcare and education. Since its inception, the foundation has endowed support to a wide range of health, socioeconomic, and education developments. Its health programs are focused on everything from basic nutrition and sanitation to malaria and tuberculosis control to HIV/AIDS and sexually transmitted disease elimination. The BMGF supports these and sundry other projects with an annual budget of about $5 billion. It provides support to the GAVI Alliance, the World Health Organization, the United Nations Children Fund, PATH Global Health Organization, and the Global Fund to Fight AIDS, Tuberculosis, and Malaria. Moreover, the foundation supports the Gates Cambridge Scholarships, which allow students and scholars from around the world to attend Cambridge University in the United Kingdom. The foundation has also received a massive boost through the various contributions provided by the entrepreneur Warren Buffet, who donated to BMFG first in 2006 and more recently in July 2018. Although the BMGF is not without its own complexities, I would challenge anyone to claim that the world is not in a better place because of the wonderful humanitarian efforts that this foundation supports. Many children throughout the world benefit from life-saving medications and vaccines provided by Merck and other companies as a result of the great-hearted donations from the BMGF.

Mr. Gates's and Mr. Buffett's efforts noted above are powerful enough, but their acts of kindness are more impressive when one considers the spark it has ignited. These donations led to the formation of the Gates-Buffet pledge, which encourages the richest individuals in the world to give away the vast majority of their fortunes to philanthropic causes. Called the Giving Pledge, the campaign has recruited over 180 signatories to date from over 20 countries. In total, the program currently has accumulated pledged donations of nearly $365 billion. In addition to Gates and Buffet, other signatories of the pledge include Mark Zuckerberg of Facebook and his wife Priscilla Chan, Carl Icahn of Icahn Enterprises, Larry Ellison of Oracle, Michael Bloomberg of Bloomberg LP, and the recently deceased Paul Allen, formerly of Microsoft and the recent Seattle Seahawks owner. These efforts support the notion that "paying it forward" is both an admirable and beneficent approach noteworthy of praise and emulation. We'll circle back to this theme in a future *Thankful Thursday* segment.

Finally, I would be a bit derelict if I did not call out the recent philanthropic efforts of Merck's former CEO, P. Roy Vagelos, and his wife, Diana. Roy served as the head of Merck Research Laboratories from 1976 to 1984 and the CEO at Merck & Co., Inc., from 1985 through 1994, and, since then, has played an instrumental role at several pharmaceutical companies, including Regeneron and Theravance. Roy is often remembered as the influential leader who helped formulate the MECTIZAN® Donation Program (MDP), wherein Merck helps provide ivermectin, free of charge, to various countries for the prevention of both river blindness and lymphatic filariasis. As Roy noted in 1987, Merck would provide ivermectin, "as much as needed, for as long as needed," through the MDP. Having celebrated its recent 30th anniversary, MDP remains a committed entity, and Merck plans to support this venture into perpetuity until these parasitic diseases are effectively eliminated from the world. But, what is even more amazing is the philanthropy that Roy and Diana have provided since 2010 via donations to various universities, including Barnard College, Washington University in St. Louis, and the Columbia College of Physicians and Surgeons (Columbia P&S), where Roy received his medical degree. Roy and Diana have given many donations along the way, but I wanted to highlight a prodigious grant of $250 million they provided to Columbia P&S in 2017. A major portion of the monies, about $150 million, will be used to endow a fund that will allow Columbia medical students who qualify for financial aid to replace their student loans with full-tuition scholarships. It is estimated that approximately a quarter of the incoming students at Columbia P&S will end up receiving full-tuition scholarships. How awesome is that! I love this story for so many reasons, foremost of which is that it reminds me of Roy and Merck's legacy, my wife Daisy, who attended medical school at Columbia P&S, and my in-laws, who met at the hospital of Columbia P&S in Harlem, NY, when they were both training for their respective degrees in medicine and nursing.

I share these examples with you today to remind you of the powerful gift of giving. In a few weeks' time, we will come upon Giving Tuesday. Unlike Black Friday and Cyber Monday, Giving Tuesday is not a commercial venture. Instead, it focuses on the importance of pledging donations during the holiday and end-of-year period, as the time of giving. This program has grown significantly over the last seven years to the point that in 2017 it is estimated that nearly 2.5 million gifts totaling $300 million were offered on that day. Not surprisingly, the program receives leadership support from the BMGF. If you choose to join the 2018 campaign, the Merck Foundation Partnership for

Giving program will match contributions of all Merck employees based in US and Puerto Rico to all eligible non-profit organizations located in these same regions. Individual donations as small as $24 or as large as $30,000 will be matched one-for-one through the Merck Gives Back website. It is so easy to sign up.

The Merck Give Back program is another example of the great Corporate responsibility that Merck maintains. As a pharmaceutical company, Merck receives a lot of "tough love" in the media (putting it lightly). The world does not always recognize nor acknowledge all the good our company does. In addition to the MDP and Merck Gives Back program, Merck provided nearly $24 million in financial contributions, medicines, and vaccines as disaster relief during the 2017 series of hurricanes, wild fires, and earthquakes. Over the last decade, our fellowships in Global Health, sponsored by the Richard T. Clark Fellowship Program, has afforded over 150 Merck employees the opportunity to work with 36 different non-profit organizations as part of three-month, field-based, corporate pro bono initiatives that are designed to help various communities around the world. Last year, Merck's Medical Outreach Program provided medicines and vaccines to over 300 thousand individuals. Finally, other programs, such as the Merck for Mothers and Neighbor of Choice programs, support both global and local efforts to change the world. We'll come back to Merck for Mothers in a future segment of *Thankful Thursdays*.

Let me close by telling you a personal story. The other night, at the dinner table in the Kartsonis-Smith household, my middle son, Sam, made an interesting, albeit provocative, statement. Somehow, we got to the topic of philanthropy, and I mentioned that I was planning to attend the Prix Galien event in New York City, which is an industry-wide celebration of newly-approved drugs, devices, and diagnostic products. I shared with the family that one philanthropist, P. Roy Vagelos, would likely be in attendance to honor two other philanthropists, Bill and Melinda Gates. At this point, Sam stated aloud that he did not believe that any individual is ever truly altruistic. That is, he feels every person does something with some selfish intent at heart, whether it is because they are hoping to curry favor, trying to avoid taxes, or because "it makes them feel that they are a better person because they have given a donation." Clearly, this is an interesting but not surprising sentiment from a 16-year old teenager who is well on his way to becoming a philosophy major and likely attorney-at-law. As you might imagine, his comment sparked a robust debate at the table about the merits and downfalls of humanitarian efforts. As I sat there listening to the fascinating discussion at the table, I was both intrigued and mystified by his argument. Clearly, despite the heroic counterpoints by his parents, Sam was not going to be moved off his original position.

It was at this point that I stopped arguing. Sam turned to me and said: "You stopped arguing because you know I'm right."

I sat back in my chair and I thought about Robert W. Woodruff. I had a sip of my Coke Zero and silently smiled, just like that once-famous Coke commercial from my childhood directed me to do.

5 The Lesson of the First Thanksgiving *(November 15, 2018)*

For this week's *Thankful Thursday* segment, I want to reflect on the first Thanksgiving that occurred in our country. With the November national holiday only a week away, it is only fitting that I offer up some of the learnings I've garnered from that event that transpired nearly 400 years ago in Plymouth, Massachusetts.

As many of you are aware, the holiday began as a day of offering gratitude for the blessing of the recent harvest and the events that transpired in the prior year. The first Thanksgiving feasts have their roots in England, where it was often common for "Days of Thanksgiving" to be offered by the Puritans in response to auspicious events or after emerging from catastrophes. For instance, such days were celebrated in England the last sixteenth century with the victory over the Spanish Armada in 1588, as well as following the end of natural disasters, such as a plague outbreak in 1604 and a brutal drought in 1611.

The event that occurred in present-day Massachusetts can be traced back to a celebration that took place in the New England colony of Plymouth in 1621. Pilgrims who emigrated to the New World from England, often as a means to escape religious persecution, brought with them the tradition of Thanksgiving. The Pilgrims had traversed the Atlantic Ocean in the *Mayflower* and landed in Plymouth in 1620 after an extremely devastating, tumultuous 66-day journey. The ensuing winter was treacherous, with only about half of the original 102 passengers surviving to see the spring. Many of the Pilgrims still lived on the ship and, under these tight conditions, suffered from scurvy and a litany of infectious diseases. When they finally moved ashore in 1621, they were greeted by a Native American named Squanto, a member of the Pawtuxet tribe, who could speak English. Squanto had previously been kidnapped by an English captain and sold into slavery in London, where he learned to speak the English language; he subsequently escaped and returned across the Atlantic to New England, only to find that his tribe had been wiped out by an epidemic. As the last of his tribe, Squanto taught the Pilgrims how to fish the Cape, cultivate maize, collect sap from maple trees, and build settlements in the new land. He also helped broker a deal with the Wampanoag tribe, which would allow for harmony and collaboration between the colonists and the Native Americans for another five decades. In recognition of the first successful corn harvest that year, the Governor of the Pilgrims, William Bradford, organized a Day of Thanksgiving in the autumn of 1621, which actually lasted for three days and included meals containing fish, mussels, clams, lobster, venison, duck, goose, swan, corn, onions, beans, spinach, cabbage, carrots, blueberries, plums, and, yes, cranberries. Notice there is no mention of turkey, potatoes, or pumpkin pie. The event, which most likely occurred in October, was attended by the about 50 Pilgrims and about 90 Native Americans, including the leader of the Wampanoag tribe, Massassoit.

Similar events would occur in the ensuing years and for nearly five decades thereafter. The traditions of these events were passed down to subsequent generations, and following the American Revolution and the ratification of the Constitution, President George Washington proclaimed the first Thanksgiving Day on November 26, 1789. Similar proclamations by other presidents and state governors would occur in subsequent years. However, the holiday as we know it today did not officially become an annual event until 1863, when President Lincoln proclaimed the last Thursday of every November to be a day of "Thanksgiving and Praise." Interestingly, Thanksgiving Day replaced another holiday known as Evacuation Day, which commemorated the last withdrawal of the British from the United States in 1783, after the American Revolution. Perhaps, with the annual commemoration of the holiday, Lincoln was trying to remind Americans, who were in the midst of the Civil War at that time, what the foundational mission of the United States was, the importance of gratitude, and the need to avoid infighting.

A week from now, many of us will gather with family, friends, and loved ones to celebrate the Thanksgiving holiday. I will be in Annapolis with my wife Daisy's family to celebrate the event. As in years past, we will undoubtedly start the day with a family football or soccer game, wherein some parent will pull a muscle and some cousin will pout over the game's outcome. It never ends well. Thereafter, we will gather for the feast. Prior to eating, my mother-in-law, Gwynneth, will mandate a moment of thanks and gratitude. In a somewhat orderly fashion, we will go around the large dining room table and each of the 15 in attendance will have to proclaim something for which they are thankful. There will be visible eye-rolls and audible sighs from the teens and tweens at the table who simply cannot comprehend why we need to partake in this annual gratitude exercise and, while we're at it, why we cannot just have the television on in the background to watch the Lions game. Eventually, all the cousins and family members will partake in this ritual, extolling their appreciation of their friends, family, Xbox Live, Snap Chat, and other wonderful things.

This year, I decided I will offer up my blessing and appreciation for all the immigrants who made this country what it is today. Ironically, when you think back to the significance of the first Thanksgiving, what defines the occasion is the fact that those English immigrants who arrived in a foreign, rugged, scary place were afforded the chance to prosper with the support and approval of the Native Americans coexisting peacefully among them. The most amazing part of the United States is that it has always been a place where those from other places could immigrate for a better livelihood or the chance to receive an education or the opportunity to escape from an oppressive existence. These immigrants brought their hopes and dreams with them, and, as a nation, we have matured and succeeded as a result of their visionary thinking, inspiration, and knack for innovation.

Let me share with you my list of seven immigrants who I'm thankful came to this country and helped to make it a better place:

1. **Alexander Hamilton**: OK, this one was a given! As a kid from the island of Nevis in the Caribbean, Alexander Hamilton emigrated to the New England colonies in 1772 and helped mold the United States, including its first government and our national mindset, into what it is today. Not only did he fight valiantly in the Revolutionary War by serving as the General Washington's secretary and ultimately leading his own battalion of troops into

the Battle of Yorktown, he also served as the First Secretary of Treasury. Unlike many of his countrymen, Hamilton realized that an agrarian nation would never be sustainable and a "nation of states" would need a strong financial foundation to succeed. His vision for a strong currency, national banks, and a federal reserve that assumed the debts of each of the 13 original states helped set the country on its course to eventual financial and industrial success. As we recently learned in a prior *Thankful Thursday* segment, he also inspired Lynn-Manuel Miranda to conceive what I believe is the greatest musical ever made. *(Honorable mention: General Gilbert du Motier, also known as the Marquis de Lafayette).*

2. **John Muir:** Born in Scotland, John Muir emigrated to the United States in 1849 when he was 11 years old. He went to college at the University of Wisconsin in Madison and thereafter traveled extensively throughout the United States. He ultimately settled in San Francisco, but his many earlier trips and the trek to California made him appreciate the natural, awe-inspiring beauty of this country. While in San Francisco, he wrote many essays and a dozen books on his adventures in nature, founded the Sierra Club, and actively advocated for the preservation of key natural sites, such as Yosemite Valley and Sequoia National Park. His efforts helped ensure the preservation of many national parks and monuments throughout the US, so that future generations might admire these stunning landscapes. *(Honorable mention: John James Audubon).*
3. **Alexander Graham Bell**: Also born in Scotland and educated at both the University of Edinburgh and University College in London, Alexander Graham Bell initially emigrated to Nova Scotia, Canada, before ultimately settling in the United States at the age of 35. He was always fascinated by speech and hearing, as both his mother and his wife were deaf. He developed hearing devices as a means to help those inflicted with such deficiencies, before ultimately parlaying his experiments into the invention of the telephone. As you sit at the dinner table next Thursday chastising your children or your friends' children for having their iPhones at the table, you can thank Mr. Bell for the mess he started. *(Honorable mention: Nikola Tesla).*
4. **Enrico Fermi:** Born in northern Italy in 1901, Enrico Fermi was trained as a physicist at the Scuola Morale Superiore in Pisa. He

emigrated to the US at the age of 37 to escape the burgeoning political unrest and the radical laws that were being enacted on minorities, including certain legislation impacting his Jewish wife. He worked on the Manhattan Project at the University of Chicago during World War II, where he developed the first nuclear reactor, called Chicago Pile-1. He then moved to Oak Ridge, Tennessee, and subsequently to Los Alamos, New Mexico, where he helped fine tune the atomic bomb effort. His war-time efforts, along with those of many others, helped end the war, ultimately ensuring that the *Man in the High Castle* could remain a fictional account. *(Honorable mention: Albert Einstein).*

5. **Levi Strauss:** Born to an Ashkenazi Jewish family in Germany in 1829, Levi Strauss emigrated to the United States at the age of 18 to join his brothers, who had begun a wholesale dry foods business in New York City. He continued in the family business for some time, with a stop along the way in Louisville, Kentucky, before heading out to San Francisco to open a West Coast business during the height of the California Gold Rush. While in California, he formed Levis Strauss and Co., which imported fine dry goods from his family in NY, including clothing and various types of household and hygiene items. With the help of one of his customers, Jacob Davis, Levi came up with the idea of developing hardy riveted denim pants that would serve as clothing for laborers to wear while performing demanding work. The famous copper rivets were added to help reinforce points of stress, such as the corner of pockets. The prototype had two pockets in the front and one on the back, with the fly in front for men and on the side for women. I'm not sure whether the original version of these blue jeans had the waist and length listed on the back, but our Levis still contain similar rivets to this day. *(Honorable mention: Andrew Carnegie).*
6. **Mary Harris Jones:** Also known as Mother Jones, this Irish-born labor leader emigrated first to Canada, and then to the US at the age of 23. She started out as a schoolteacher and eventually became a dressmaker. Unfortunately, in 1867 when she was 30, an epidemic of yellow fever hit the city of Memphis and she lost her husband and all four children, all of whom were under the age of 5. She moved to Chicago, only to have her dress shop destroyed in the Great Chicago Fire of 1871. But instead of wallowing in her misery, she helped rebuild the city, where she witnessed the massive abuses of workers by corporations. The next 60 years

of her life would be dedicated to helping to organize workers throughout the country to protest the treacherous conditions in mines and factories. Her efforts helped galvanize the development of child labor laws that remain in effect today *(Honorable mention: Madeline Albright).*

7. **Jay Ajayi**: Born in London, England in 1993 to Nigerian parents, Jay Ajayi moved to the United States with his family when he was seven years old. Settling first in Maryland and then in Texas, he played sports throughout high school. In his senior year, he was the star running back for the football team at Frisco Liberty High School, where he led the team with a whopping 35 touchdowns. He went on to attend college and play football at Boise State in Idaho, where he played three years on their famous blue field and was a spectacular running back. Although he was a top talent, he was not drafted into the NFL until the fifth round, partly because of an arrest early in college for stealing a pair of sweatpants from Walmart. He noted that the five days he spent in jail for that transgression gave him a new sense of humility that would ultimately help drive him forward to succeed even in the face of adversity. Halfway through 2017's NFL season, Jay was traded to the Philadelphia Eagles, a team which he would help catapult to a Super Bowl championship. He averaged close to six years per carry in 2017 as an Eagle. *(Honorable mention: Ben Simmons and Joel Embiid).*

OK, maybe that last one is a bit too much, but since it is my list, I can choose to include whoever I want. I did not include Merck's first CEO and a German immigrant, George F. Merck. His legacy deserves more than just a short blurb, so we'll come back to him in a future *Thankful Thursday* segment.

If you think about it, we are essentially all here in the United States because either our distant ancestors, our parents or grandparents, or we ourselves made the courageous, daunting leap of faith to migrate to this nation. My wife, Daisy, can trace her family back to the *Mayflower*, and thus she is veritable Daughter of the American Revolution. I, on the other hand, am a first generation American, as the child of two Greek immigrants who came to the United States in the 1950-1960s. As I quipped at the rehearsal dinner of our wedding: "Our two merging families, The Kartsonis and the Smith family, are really one and the same. We both came over to the US as immigrants in boats. One small difference: Daisy's family on the *Mayflower*, a few centuries ago, and my family on the rusty boat that is still harbored off the docks of New York City."

Let's never forget that someone gave us or our predecessors a chance to revel in the cornucopia of delights and wonders that this country has to offer. I wake up each day reminding myself that I was born in the United States, but my parents, just one generation earlier, were born in a more frightening place during an era of sheer poverty, unrest, and uncertainty. Their incredible sacrifices afforded me the opportunity to be where I am today. If this is not enough to be thankful for, then frankly I do not know what is.

In closing, I hope each of you have a wonderful Thanksgiving holiday. Please take some time to celebrate everything you are grateful for with your loved ones. Until next time, I'm giving you each the assignment to pass on your own *Thankful Thursday* message on Thanksgiving Day to those around you.

6 A Gift from St. Nick *(December 6, 2018)*

For this week's *Thankful Thursday* segment, I want to pay gratitude to **St. Nick** for the wonderful gift he has given me this year.

OK, for you to understand what I'm getting at, I need to take a step back and explain a little bit about the concept of name days and why today is the day we celebrate St. Nick.

I was raised in a very Greek family. Growing up Greek comes with many wonderful attributes. For starters, Greek food is zesty, delicious, and plentiful. Additionally, Greek people are fervently proud of their heritage. Many Greeks raise their families with a strong respect of Hellenistic history, culture, and community, ultimately conjuring up a sense of uniqueness for many Greek Americans. And, then, finally, there are the name days.

A name day is a tradition celebrated by Orthodox and Catholic individuals in certain countries, including many in Europe—Greece, Italy, France, Spain, the Netherlands, and most Scandinavian and Eastern European countries—and Latin America—Uruguay and Argentina. Essentially, it involves celebrating a particular day in the year that is associated with one's given name. This tradition, which traces back to the Middle Ages, stems from the Christian calendar of saints, with individuals celebrating their name day at the same time that the Church celebrates a particular saint's feast day. In the Greek Orthodox tradition, this is usually the day a saint has died, so this event serves as a commemoration of their life spent in service of a religious pursuit or a theological calling. I have always loved name days because they are in many ways equivalent to having a second birthday. The Greeks celebrate the day with much fanfare and with all the pleasantries of a birthday but with one notable exception: there is no cake. That aside, it is a pretty awesome event because everyone visits you, they celebrate you with a huge feast, and then, best of all for a kid, they give you loads of presents. The best present is cold hard cash, or, as some of my Greek friends would refer to it, pocket money. I like to think they called it that because you often needed to accept the cash very quickly before your parents would notice, intercede, and demand that the amount was simply too much. Parents would argue that it was not possible for you to accept that much cash from your Uncle Gus or Aunt Aphrodite; they would usually then try to make you give it back. However, if you were smart and learned to quickly place this money in your pocket, none of the awkwardness that comes with your being told to give it back would ever ensue. (Invariably, the adult gift givers would refuse to accept its return and, in the end, you still ended up with the money). It's basically Greek theater, and the Greeks have a lot of practice in this area, dating back over 2,500 years to the days of Euripides, Sophocles, and Aristophanes.

So, with that backdrop, you should all know that today, December 6, is the name day for all individuals named Nicholas, Nick, or any other related version (Niki, Nicole, Nicola, etc.). St. Nicholas Day is a holiday celebrated by many cultures besides the Greeks. The day also honors the Christian bishop Nicholas of Myra. Surprising as it may seem, we all know about the legend of this wonderful saint, but perhaps not in its original context. So, let me take a moment to place it in its proper context. Born sometime around 280 AD in Patara, which is now part of Turkey, St. Nicholas grew up an orphan, having lost both parents early in his life. His parents were relatively wealthy at the time of their passing, and their inheritance was passed on to Nicholas. However, instead of choosing to live a life of luxury, Nicholas was extremely devout and opted to give away his inheritance to the needy, the poor, and the suffering. There are many legendary stories of how Nicholas helped others, but one that involves three poor sisters has gained much fame. Nicholas learned that the parents of three young women lacked the means to provide them a dowry for marriage, an important custom at those times, so Nicholas snuck secretly into their house late at night on three separate occasions and left a bag of silver coins inside their home. Each time, the money was found and used to help generate a dowry for the daughters. As luck might have it,

Nicholas was caught by the father on the third occasion, at which point the home owner, so touched by the gesture, got down on his knees and thanked him profusely for his kindness. His humble existence and renowned generosity in support of the impoverished earned Nicholas an appointment to bishop in the town of Myra, now known as Demre, in Turkey. He died on December 6 in the year 343 AD. However, his legacy lived on, and eventually the Church consecrated him as a saint for his miracles of philanthropy.

The story of St. Nicholas's gift-giving became very popular throughout many parts of Europe, and although many western European countries turned away from celebrating saints during the Protestant reformation, the Netherlands held on to this tradition. Dutch children celebrated the occasion by putting their shoes outside their homes the night of December 5. Amazingly, the next day, the children would discover them filled with gifts left by St. Nicholas, or as they referred to him in Dutch, "Sinterklass". In the sixteenth and seventeenth centuries, the Dutch colonists brought this tradition to the United States, and particularly to Dutch Pennsylvania; as a result, the annual gift-giving ritual became very popular in the United States. After many transformations, Sinterklaas came to be known as "Santa Claus" and the tradition of gift giving on the Christmas holiday went viral (by the way, "viral" will be the only reference to infectious diseases in this *Thankful Thursday* segment). Over time, the celebration got moved back to December 25 to correspond with the end of the year holiday season. All that said, the Greeks, the Dutch, and many others celebrate December 6 as the name day for St. Nicholas, the greatest gift-giver of all.

By the way, the idea that Santa Claus wore red is not true. St. Nicholas of Myra was not known for wearing red. This is a myth started by the cartoonist Thomas Nast in an 1881 caricature of Santa Claus. The cartoonist felt that Santa Claus looked jollier dressed in a red suit.

Well, amazingly, the tradition of celebrating St. Nick is still alive today in the United States, and especially in the Pennsylvania region. So, today, it is fitting that I, along with all my local Pennsylvanian brethren, proclaim my thanks and gratitude for St. Nick and the wonderful gift he gave me this year. I guess at this point, you are all sitting there reading this in front of your computer screens or your iPhones, sipping your coffee and scratching your head on this cold Thursday morning, wondering: Where is he taking this?

I'm thankful for the greatest Nick the state of Pennsylvania has ever seen.

Yes, I'm grateful for Nicholas Edward Foles and his gift of "silver," also known as the Lombardi Trophy. That gift, which was proffered ten months ago, was a Super Bowl championship for the NFL's greatest franchise, the Philadelphia Eagles. The Eagles won their first Super Bowl championship on a blustery cold Minnesotan day, on February 5, 2018, to be exact. When I turned 50 years of age a month later, I was not in want of any presents. The greatest gift I could ever have received was the knowledge that my beloved "Iggles" were the Super Bowl champions. Nonetheless, my family and friends showered me with wonderful gifts, including various clothing items adorned with Philadelphia Eagles Super Bowl champion memorabilia, a Vineyard Vines® cloth belt with the Eagles insignia, multiple portraits of the Eagles newspaper headlines on the day after the Super Bowl win, and a Super Bowl football signed by a number of Eagles' players, including Carson Wentz, Corey Clement, Zach Ertz, Alshon Jeffrey, Jay Ajayi, and you guessed it, Nick Foles.

I love the Nick Foles story for many reasons, but here are my top five reasons as to why I laud him for today's segment:

1. **Hungry Dogs Run Fast**: Nobody gave the Eagles a snowball's chance in hell to win the Super Bowl, let alone actually get there to compete for the championship. After Carson Wentz went down with a season-ending knee tear a year ago, the Eagles were counted out and listed as the underdogs in each of their three playoff games. As all-pro Eagles offensive lineman Jason Kelce would tell the crowd at the Super Bowl championship parade, the team embraced the underdog status because, well, "hungry dogs run fast" (**Figure 4**). All those prognosticators also forgot that we had a secret weapon in Nick Foles. Not only did Nick deliver several key wins in late December to clinch home field advantage, but he also dished up three impressive wins in an improbable run through the playoffs. In the three playoff games, Nick completed 72 percent of his passes for nearly 1,000 total yards and six touchdowns, for an awe-inspiring passer rating of 115.7. For all you non-football aficionados, that's really, really good.
2. **Resiliency**: What makes this achievement even more incredible is that Nick Foles almost quit playing football altogether not too long ago. After being traded to the St. Louis Rams, Nick lost the

zeal for the game and actually asked for and was granted release from that team. However, after a fishing trip with his brother-in-law, he decided to give the NFL one more go and joined the Kansas City Chiefs for the 2016 season. Luckily, the Eagles front office had the foresight to sign him in the offseason after the 2016 year, and the rest is history. Nick is indeed a story of perseverance and resilience.

3. **Precision Passing**: In a run of three playoff games, Nick Foles threw some of the most jaw-dropping passes I've ever seen completed in football. It will take me too long to chronicle them all—rest assured, I could—but I do want to point out three key ones: (1) the flea-flicker tight spiral to Torrey Smith at the left pylon over two Vikings defenders in the NFL championship game, (2) the over-the-top toss to Alshon Jeffrey over another former Eagle in the first quarter of the Super Bowl, and (3) the needle-threading pass to Corey Clement in the back of the end zone in the third quarter of the Super Bowl (and, yes, that was a catch!). Oh yeah, there's one more pass I forgot to mention. That would be the one that went off the knee of Falcons' safety Keanu Neal into the waiting hands of Torrey Smith in the first playoff game. I'd like to think that last one was inspired by some divine intervention, perhaps from St. Nicholas.

4. **Boldness and Humility:** Another reason I laud Nick Foles is that he is responsible for calling the greatest play in Philadelphia sports history. With less than one minute before halftime in the Super Bowl and the Eagles facing a fourth and one on the New England Patriot goal line, Nick convinced Coach Doug Pederson to call a trick play that will go down in the lore of football greatness: "Hey, you want Philly Philly?" (**Figure 5**). Not only was the play call bold, but the fact Coach Pederson readily accepted the suggestion proved what an incredibly humble team leader Doug is for this organization. Humility is a superpower, and Doug exhibited it brilliantly. The play is so memorable that they even carved it into a tall bronze statue outside of Lincoln Financial Field. On that play, we also learned one other important thing: Not only can Nick pass, he can also catch the ball as well. Unlike some other quarterback in New England who will remain nameless, Nick proved that when his team needed him most, he was not about to drop the ball.

5. **Family First:** Finally, my favorite memory of the whole Super Bowl celebration is seeing Nick hugging his wife and holding his beautiful one-year-old daughter, Lily, on the Super Bowl stage. Dressed in her jeans jacket, a bright green bow in her hair, and headphones way too large for her head, Lily was taking it all in. For sure, she was the belle at the ball during the post-game celebration. She also sparked a recent uptick of little girls being born in the Philadelphia area with the name Lily. Aside from Lily, Nick still had one more thing to lift up, and that was the Lombardi Trophy. Oh yeah, and the Super Bowl MVP trophy too.

So, today, I am thankful for my Greek heritage, for my name day celebration, and for the sheer coincidence that I have the same name as the greatest gift-giver that has ever lived in Philadelphia. I think it only fitting that our shared first name is derived from a Greek word; the name *"Nicholas"* is indeed a combination of two Greek words, *niki* and *laos.* Together, they signify the "victor of the people." Yep, that sounds about right for the Eagles back-up quarterback who wears #9.

For many years, Philadelphia Eagles fans have lived with the misery and disappointment of never winning a Super Bowl. They have been repeatedly berated, chastised, and mocked for being the worst NFL fans. It seems like a week does not pass without some national talking head reminding Eagles fans how horrible they are: "Aren't these the same fans that threw snowballs at Santa Claus?" Indeed, I must confess that this infamous snowball-throwing event, which occurred 50 years ago this month on December 15, 1968, is true. After a miserable 2-12 season that year, the Eagles fans were in no mood to celebrate the 1968 holiday season during the last home game that year at Franklin Field. The ill-fated decision to parade out a fake Santa Claus was just a recipe for disaster. Ironically enough, that Santa was pulled from the stands during a halftime celebration because the commissioned Santa failed to show due to the blistering snow storm. But now, we know the real reason for the fans' dastardly act: The Eagles fans threw those snowballs because they had the foresight to know that he was not the real Santa Claus.

All along, Eagles fans knew the real St. Nick would come. The real Santa Claus is not some guy you can just pluck from the stands. The real Santa Claus is not just any dude dressed in a red suit. The real Santa Claus is none other than jolly St. Nick (Foles). The Eagles fan base had to wait another 50 years to realize this, but it was well worth the wait. St. Nick would give me and all Eagles fans a gift worth waiting for. Thanks, #9, for the awesome present!

Somewhere, I know St. Nicholas of Myra is smiling. Although red and green are the traditional holiday colors, I can promise you St. Nicholas is not wearing a red suit because he does not cheer for the New England Patriots. He would never deign to wear a color adorned by that team. St. Nicholas doesn't even root for the New Orleans Saints. St Nicholas is a die-hard Eagles fan, and you can bet your bottom dollar that he looks so much jollier wearing a Midnight Green jersey with a big number 9 on it.

As the renowned Eagles play-by-play announcer Merrill Reese would say, Let's Go Eagles!

7 A Serenade for the Seasonal Shutdown *(December 20, 2018)*

For this week's *Thankful Thursday* segment (the last *Thankful Thursday* of 2018), I want to take a moment to express my gratitude for the year-end Holiday shutdown and the time it affords me to reflect on all the outstanding, scientific accomplishments made in 2018.

Every living thing on this earth needs some downtime. As living beings, our cells will grow, mature, age, and, in most cases, be replaced over time, but none of this is possible unless our organs, as well as our whole human body, take a periodic respite.

I like to refer to this as human "diastole."

Why, you might ask?

Well, it is only fitting that we learn from one organ that supposedly never stops working, namely the heart. A person who maintains an average heartbeat of 75 beats per minute will ultimately have their heart pump 108,000 times a day. Assuming that same individual lives to the jolly old age of 90 years, their heart will have contracted approximately 3.5 billion times in their lifetime. But, what is truly amazing is the incredible cardiac machine always takes a break after each beat. In essence, the heart muscle must contract to carry out the function of pushing blood out (systole), but then it must immediately relax in order to allow blood back in (diastole). This dilation phase of diastole, so appropriately termed after the Greek word for dilation (διαστολή), is the cycle during which the muscles surrounding the two ventricles relax, thereby allowing ventricular refilling and subsequent dilation. Amazingly, what many of us do not know is that heart actually rests more than it works. If we consider that same individual whose heart averages 75 beat per minute, their entire cycle of systole/diastole would be about 0.8 seconds. For each cycle, the heart remains in systole for 0.3 seconds, while diastole takes 0.5 seconds. So, in essence, the heart really rests 63 percent of the time. Even this ever-working organ realizes the importance of a periodic interruption. Our respiratory system, which works in an analogous way, also has learned to take a breather after each work cycle.

Many of our other organs besides the heart and lungs will also take a pause periodically throughout the day and especially during periods of rest, such as sleep. During sleep, the decrease in use of oxygen by some of our vital organs allows for energy to be diverted to the growth of new cells in our muscle, bone, or bone marrow. Our dormant period is also the time for tissue repair and peptide/protein formation. Interestingly, many of us think about sleep as the time our brain rests, and although there is some truth to this point, it is not entirely a period of cerebral inactivity. Sleep is also an active period during which our neurons undergo critical processing, restoration, and strengthening. During sleep, these neuronal cells are actually working to solidify and consolidate memories we have gathered during our hectic day. Although we take in an incredible amount of information during the active periods of our day, much of this information is not processed and stored until sleep takes hold. While we sleep, the process of consolidation occurs, wherein the information gathered during our many interactions during the wake periods of the day gets transferred from its tentative short-term state into longer-term memory. So, healthy sleep is required each and every day because we need to afford the brain the consolidation time it requires to take it all in.

So, I hope I've provided some scientific, biological perspective as to why, as humans, we cannot be running at full capacity at all times. Our organs need time to rest, thereby affording our entire body as well as our mind a necessary holiday. This is exactly the reason we only work certain hours in a particular day and only so many hours in a week. This also highlights why certain interruptions during the day, or lulls away from work, are so critical; studies have shown that taking periodic recess during the work day to have a pleasant chat or have lunch with a colleague paradoxically increases productivity by helping lift one's mood, avoid mental stagnation, and increase one's creative fuel. As some of you might know, I'm a big believer in exercising each day while I'm at work. Indeed, studies have shown that a moderate level of cardiac activity, such as a trip to the gym or a walk outside, can boost one's ingenuity, creativity, and productivity for as much as two to three hours afterward. The change in scenery is often the unanticipated impetus one needs to have a breakthrough (aha!) moment at work in helping to address an issue or overcome an obstacle.

Some even espouse the concept of the power nap. In a recently published book entitled *When*, the author, Daniel Pink, promotes the virtues of the "nappuchino," wherein a person drinks a cup a coffee immediately before laying their head down for about 20 minutes; the quick nap helps to rejuvenate the body, and the caffeine boost, which usually requires 20 minutes to take hold, sets one up perfectly to awake refreshed and on a positive mission ready to take on a new challenge. In any case, the worst thing that one can do is work continuously throughout the day with no breaks. In fact, if the work gods will permit, I try to block off the following times for my own personal work day: the 6 o'clock hour (for exercise), the 12 o'clock hour (for lunch and a quick stroll around the office), and the 4 o'clock hour (for close-out work and to return phone calls). While at work, I encourage each of you to pause to enjoy a solemn period of quiescence.

Many of the same principles apply when considering a more protracted, dedicated time away from our chaotic jobs. The power that comes from an additional day off, a long weekend, and, most importantly, a vacation away from the office is enormous. Prolonged time out of the office helps to recharge and rejuvenate our wearied bodies, to reconnect us with our more innovative side, and to provide a period of reflection on career purpose; in essence, a vacation serves as an excellent reminder as to why we come to work after all. From my perspective, everyone earns their vacation, and I would argue that if you do not take the necessary time off to have a true vacation, then the only person you can blame is the individual staring back at you in the mirror. I learned about five years into my career at Merck that I was so much more optimistic, relaxed, and rejuvenated if I took a two-week vacation in the summer. After the 14-day get-away, I would return energized, refreshed, and happy; it also made me appreciate my job even more. So, the two-week time away from the office in July or August has become a non-negotiable norm of my existence.

My father used to say a funny thing in Greek: "Nobody's tombstone will ever read: I wish I worked harder." Not surprisingly, many European cultures, like the one my Greek father was accustomed to, have long advocated for daily siestas as a tool to recharge each day, and long holidays as a vehicle to reconnect with your life outside of work. In fact, my father, who owned his own dry-cleaning shop, use to hire someone to come mind the store from noon to 3 PM daily, at which point he drove home, ate lunch, and partook in an hour-long nap before returning to work for another three hours to finish the day. As we also know from observing our colleagues across the Atlantic, many Europeans also advocate for long summer holidays, usually for the entire month of August, where they travel to visit family or friends in other parts of Europe or the world. Based on everything I told you above, it should not come as an earth-shattering surprise to learn that despite such measures, such as siestas and longer holiday seasons, our European colleagues remain just as productive as Americans.

So, on this backdrop, I'd like to use this last *Thankful Thursday* segment of the 2018 calendar year to proclaim my enormous appreciation, heartfelt gratitude, and frank adoration for a relatively recent company invention—the Merck Holiday shutdown. As many of you who have been employed by Merck for some time know, the company made a critical decision a little less than a decade ago to institute a year-end holiday shutdown, wherein the US offices would close for the week between December 24, Christmas Eve, and January 1, New Year's Day. In the first year of the program, I was a bit dismayed to still receive emails from colleagues during this time, but as the years progressed and senior leaders were asked to serve as exemplars, Merck employees truly began to separate from their jobs during the shutdown period. From my perspective, the holiday shutdown is the quintessential time of relaxation and recalibration. It serves as the one extended time of the year where we all separate from our jobs. Amazingly, the company still survives during this time, even without us feverishly checking Microsoft Outlook, Sync, or Jabber.

So, as you take time off this holiday shutdown season, please reconnect with your family, other loved ones, and old acquaintances outside of work. Take the time to relish in your favorite pastimes, whether it be holiday caroling with dear friends, binge-watching Netflix in front of a cozy fire, reading a really trashy novel until 2 AM, snorkeling off some fancy tropical island in the Caribbean, or skiing on some radically soft powder in Jackson Hole. I plan to read a few biographies, see John Oliver perform, visit a few local colleges with my middle son, and watch the endless array of college football games that ESPN has to offer.

As you partake in your most treasured pleasures over the holiday shutdown, please take a breather to reminisce about the incredible achievement that the Vaccines and Infectious Disease teams within Merck have accomplished over the last 12 months. Any valiant effort I would undertake to list them all here would be a fruitless attempt, as this segment is already long enough, and the accomplishments are too many to enumerate. Moreover, I could not adequately do each team justice. That said, I'm grateful for all the advancements made in the past year in the treatment and prevention of human immunodeficiency virus, bacterial and fungal infections, *Clostridium difficile* infection, and cytomegalovirus (CMV) disease, to name a few. On the Vaccines front, our advancement of vaccines to tackle diseases such as human papillomavirus, *Streptococcus pneumoniae* (pneumococcus), CMV, dengue, and, of course, Ebola are noteworthy.

Have a happy, healthy, and safe holiday season. May all your wishes for a joyful and peaceful 2019 come true!

8 Our Bold Approach to Ebola *(January 10, 2019)*

Welcome to a new year and a fresh start to *Thankful Thursdays*.

For this week's *Thankful Thursday* segment, I want to voice my gratitude to the V920 (Ebola Vaccine) team on a major accomplishment: the submission of the preclinical, clinical, and preliminary CMC dossier to support a rolling review by the United States Food and Drug Administration (FDA).

Merck has initiated the rolling submission for the licensing application for V920. As Merck noted publicly via a press release, the initial dossier was submitted in the fourth quarter of 2018. Although this dossier will be supplemented with additional data over the next six to nine months, the initiation of the Health Authority review across all three components of the V920 dossier—preclinical, clinical, and quality—is a significant milestone worthy of praise. Hence, it is only fitting that we start the 2019 year off right with a tribute to V920 and the devoted, sedulous team who have brought us to this point.

But before we discuss V920, it is essential that we take a step back and tell the story from its rightful beginning. To do so, we need to travel back in time to 1976.

That year, the United States was celebrating the bicentennial anniversary of our country. Admittedly, the only vivid memory that I have of that year was the celebration of our country's birthday in the New York harbor. As a little 8-year-old, wide-eyed boy growing up in northern New Jersey, I can still remember my parents taking me that Independence Day to the western Palisades cliffs of the Hudson River, just a few miles south of the George Washington Bridge, to watch the tall ships pass by the Statue of Liberty. Indeed, 1976 was a hallmark year on many fronts. That year, a short, studious, peanut farmer from Plains, Georgia, would be catapulted in the limelight to win the US presidential election. Athletes like Bruce Jenner and Nadia Comaneci would dazzle us with their performances at the summer Olympics in Montreal. A rough, urban class band from Dublin called U2 would get its start in 1976, while, at the same time, a few young entrepreneurs would initiate a tiny start-up company developing Apple computers out of a garage in Los Altos, California. That same year, George Lucas would begin filming a low-budget film in Tunisia about a space battle in a galaxy far, far away. The Concorde supersonic jet would begin to operate across the Atlantic, while a show about a lovable green frog named Kermit would ascend to an instant TV hit.

But, 1976 was not without its horrors, and, in fact, many would argue that the year wherein we celebrated our nation's 200th birthday was indeed scary on many fronts. Early that year, the Lutz family decided to abandon their haunted home at 112 Ocean Avenue in Amityville, New York, after living there for only 28 days. Apparently, the family was not willing to share the home with the prior owners. Later that year, in July, delegates attending an American Legion conference at the famous Bellevue-Stratford Hotel on Broad Avenue in Philadelphia would fall ill from a respiratory condition caused by a previously undescribed, atypical bacterium. By the time it was all over, 29 conference attendees would die from pneumonia, later determined to be attributed to *Legionella pneumophilia*. But, the scariest event that took place that year did not even occur in the United States. What I'm referring to was an unusual outbreak of a new infection in sub-Saharan Africa. In fact, two separate outbreaks of what appeared to be the same infection took place, nearly simultaneously, in the neighboring countries of Sudan and Zaire in the Congo. By the time these two infections were contained, over 600 individuals would fall ill and 430 would fatally succumb to the infection. The infection, which first struck a school headmaster in Zaire (now known as the Democratic Republic of the Congo (DRC)), occurred in a small village called Yambuku, which is located on the banks of the Ebola River. Hence, this disease, which spread rapidly throughout that village's hospital, was referred to as Ebola Disease.

The most difficult aspect of this new infection was its close resemblance in disease presentation to other infections that occur in the same region. Ebola virus disease (EVD), also known as Ebola hemorrhagic fever (EHF) or simply Ebola, routinely presents with non-descript features of fever, sore throat, fatigue, headache, and muscle aches. It is only as the infection progresses several days later that one begins to see the development of nausea, vomiting, diarrhea, and rash. Thereafter, internal and external bleeding may take hold, and the patient can progress into shock, organ failure, and a comatose state. In most cases, as there is no approved treatment for EVD, the disease will carry a mortality rate of over 50 percent. Yet, at the time of initial presentation, the infection can look very similar to influenza or other non-descript viral infections; moreover, it presents similarly to other common infections seen in the Congo, such as malaria, dengue, or other blood-producing fevers. Hence, early diagnosis and infection control measures are critical, as the infection is highly contagious to humans if they are exposed to bodily fluids (blood, urine, vomitus, saliva) from an infected individual.

Over time, scientists would uncover that the EVD was caused by an RNA, single-stranded virus from the filovirus family of viruses. We would learn that the fruit bat is the natural host of this virus, and eating bush meat infected by the virus can lead to EVD. Virologists would also eventually uncover the pathophysiology of this deadly disease. The medical community would learn that, as the virus invades the body, it infects various blood cells and sets up shop in the lymph nodes. From there, new virus particles are released into the bloodstream and can infect cells lining blood vessels, the liver, and other organs. As Ebola infects blood cells that naturally provide immunity against microorganisms, these cells often undergo programmed cell death, leading to a reduced immune response. Certain other infected cells, like those lining our blood vessels, lose their adhesive properties as a result of damage caused directly and indirectly by the viral outer protein, resulting in bleeding and the eventual activation of a dysfunctional clotting cascade. Over time, molecular biologists would discover that the filamentous viruses that caused the two outbreaks in 1976 were actually caused by two distinct viruses with different genomic sequences within the genus of Ebola virus; these two viruses were named for the region of their first outbreak, Sudan virus (SUDV) and the Zaire Ebola virus (ZEBOV). Eventually, another three strains of the Ebola genus would be identified, including two that cause infections in all primates Bundibugyo virus (BDBV) and Taï Forest virus (TAFV); the latter also known as the Ivory Coast virus) and one that caused infections in non-human primates only (Reston virus (RESTV)). The infections resembled closely those caused by another filovirus, Marburg virus, which was so named for the town in Germany where that infection first was discovered in 1967.

Altogether, Ebola viruses would account for 28 different outbreaks between 1976 and the present day, including nine "major" outbreaks infecting at least 100 individuals. Notably, 18 of the 28 outbreaks, and eight of the nine "major outbreaks" were caused by ZEBOV; in fact, the only "major" outbreak not caused by ZEBOV was one of the two original 1976 infections which started in Nzara, Sudan and caused by SUDV. Yet, of all the outbreaks that have occurred to date, the one that moved the world to action was the one that transpired between 2014 and 2016 in West Africa, predominantly in the countries of Sierra Leone, Liberia, and Guinea. By the time that epidemic was controlled, ZEBOV would infect over 28,000 individuals and result in the death of over 11,000 victims. It was in the midst of this epidemic, as the world grappled with the fears of Ebola, that Merck made the corporate decision to lend its support to the effort.

Recognizing our expertise in infectious disease small molecule and vaccine development, and specifically in the manufacturing of live viral vaccines, Merck searched the landscape as to how it might assist the venture. We learned of a small company, NewLink Genetics (NLG) Corporation, based in Iowa, that was developing an attenuated live vaccine against Ebola in close partnership with the vaccine developers from the Public Health Agency of Canada (PHAC). Together, they were advancing an innovative, unique vaccine platform to prevent Ebola infections. Their vaccine is a live-attenuated, replication-competent version of a vesicular stomatitis virus (VSV); VSV is an excellent vector to use because it normally does not cause human infection. Within its viral RNA, the gene that makes the normal outer covering of VSV glycoprotein G was recombinantly switched with the gene encoding for Ebola glycoprotein, thereby resulting in the display of Ebola glycoproteins on a viral construct of VSV.

Hence, when the vaccine (known formally as rVSVΔG-ZEBOV-GP) is given to a person, that individual develops protective, neutralizing antibodies (nAb) to the Ebola glycoprotein without succumbing to the clinical symptoms of EVD. Through the dedicated support of the United States National Institute of Health (NIH) and a retinue of other sponsors, NLG demonstrated that the vaccine was immunogenic and 100 percent effective in a non-human primate challenge study. Together, these partners initiated eight different Phase 1 studies in healthy volunteers demonstrating that robust nAb responses against Ebola could be developed in healthy volunteers; in fact, we now know that these immunogenic responses persist for at least two years. Then, in the midst of the 2014-2016 epidemic, NLG worked diligently to make the vaccine available in the region through emergency use protocols. Very large studies were initiated in Liberia, led by the NIH (PREVAIL trial), Sierra Leone, led by the United States Center for Disease Control and Prevention (STRIVE trial), and Guinea, led by the World Health Organization (*Ebola Ca Suffit* trial), to try to prevent future cases of EVD.

The latter of these three studies, the Ebola Ca Suffit study, warrants further discussion. Ebola Ca Suffit, which translates brilliantly to "Ebola, that's enough," was an elegantly-designed ring vaccination trial, wherein all subjects who had EVD were carefully evaluated to identify all their recent contacts and the contacts of those recent contacts. All the individuals tied to single person with EVD made up a cluster. This "ring vaccination" approach was used successfully in the early 1970s to help in the eventual elimination of small pox. The Ebola Ca Suffit study would ultimately randomize 185 different clusters (involving about 12,000 individuals) either to immediate vaccination at randomization or delayed vaccination 21 days following randomization to determine whether the vaccine could prevent new cases of EVD. Amazingly, the study demonstrated that those receiving the Ebola vaccine in the immediate vaccination group had no cases of EVD, as compared to 10-16 cases of EVD observed in various populations of subjects included in the delayed vaccination group. In essence, the vaccine demonstrated 100 percent efficacy.

Although NLG did marvelous work to support the early development efforts, it was apparent that they needed assistance to bring this vaccine over the finish line. That is when Merck stepped in. Merck signed an agreement with NLG in November 2014, while the ongoing outbreak was proceeding in West Africa and during the early conduct of the three large emergency-use protocols. Working with NLG, Merck instituted a plan to prepare the vaccine for licensure. This was no small feat.

So, what exactly did Merck do?

First, Merck brought in the data from the various earlier studies in animals and humans. This was a Herculean feat, as it required the meticulous transfer of precious clinical samples across the world, often under the tightly-regulated, cold chain conditions. Our company then took the data and reports from these earlier studies and retrofitted them to meet regulatory standard. All the while, Merck closely collaborated with Health Authorities to garner agreement on the requirements for licensure. As part of these regulatory efforts, Merck expanded the development of immunogenicity assays to support the testing of the samples collected from the prior studies. In the midst of these measures, the Company also supported the scale-up activities of the manufacturing of the vaccine to allow for the completion of a lot consistency study in an effort to demonstrate the vaccine production could be performed using a reliable process. On the capital front, Merck identified, initiated, and built a new commercial manufacturing site where the final approved vaccine could be developed. Finally, Merck compiled the complicated dossier for submission to the Health Authorities to support V920's licensure. This required a meticulous review of all the available preclinical and clinical data, including the evolving safety data from the three large West African studies. Ultimately, the submission included data from nearly 16,000 vaccinated subjects recruited into 12 different clinical trials.

More impressively, Merck prepared investigational vaccine for use in the event of future Ebola outbreaks, even ahead of licensure. A large supply of V920 was developed over the last few years to support two separate outbreaks in the DRC, one of which is still ongoing in the eastern portion of the DRC. This required tight coordination of vaccine supply to ensure it was delivered to the region using proper conditions and accurate authorization under the tight constraints of existing protocols. Notably, Merck managed all these activities while under the constant scrutiny of the world.

These accomplishments could have never been realized without the support of the large cadre of V920 team members throughout our company. Today, I want to take a moment to thank the entire V920 team for all its steadfast commitment to this task. I would be remiss if I did not also acknowledge the incredible efforts of all our partners, including NGL, PHAC, the US Biomedical Advanced Research and Development Authority (BARDA), the US Department of Defense, the Global Alliance for Vaccines and Immunization (GAVI), World Health Organization, Medicins sans Frontiers/Doctors Without Borders, the numerous Health Authorities, including the US FDA and the European Union Committee for Medicinal Products for Human Use (CHMP), and many, many others. Clearly, it takes a village to develop a vaccine, and the members that make up this village have toiled fervently to ensure that many villages in Africa can have a crucial tool to stave off this deadly disease.

Let's be frank. Vaccine development is never easy. There's a reason why only a few pharmaceutical companies choose to invest in this arena, and why generic manufacturers often shy away from vaccine investments. Such development is particularly daunting and challenging when conducted under tight timelines, extensive scrutiny, and the involvement of multiple partners. Although Merck has gratefully received financial support from BARDA and the United States Department of Defense Threat Reduction Program and Joint Vaccination Acquisition Program to develop V920, Merck still needed to invest extensively in this program. Moreover, the decision to invest in V920, as opposed to other endeavors, comes with an opportunity cost that is rarely acknowledged and will never be recouped. I would also candidly admit that V920 is not a perfect vaccine; it only covers ZEBOV and must be packaged, frozen, and stored at -70°C. Just take a second to contemplate what measures must be instituted to ensure the vaccine is delivered into small sub-equatorial villages located in remote sub-Saharan regions. Despite this, our company chose to advance V920 even when we knew that the vaccine would never be profitable for Merck or our stockholders. We have committed to providing the vaccine to the world's poorest countries at the lowest price possible. Merck has led this effort because we had the capacity, intellectual know-how, and corporate responsibility to do the right thing. In a world where talk is cheap and pharmaceutical companies are often villainized for rising drug prices, the decision Merck made to tackle the problem tacitly speaks volumes.

I leave you with the fitting words of George W. Merck, speaking to students at the Medical College of Virginia at their Founders' Day celebration on December 1, 1950: "We try to remember that medicine is for the patient. We try never to forget that medicine is for the people. It is not for the profits....How can we bring the best of medicine to each and every person? We cannot rest until the way has been found, with our help, to bring our finest achievements to everyone."[9] Clearly, George W. Merck would be proud of all you have done to bring V920 one step closer to becoming a reality.

9 From the speech "Medicine is for the Patient, Not for the Profits"

9 E Pluribus Unum
(January 17, 2019)

For this week's *Thankful Thursday* segment, I want to express my appreciation for all those who have worked tirelessly to unite us, despite all our inherent differences. As we embark upon the commemoration of Martin Luther King Jr., next Monday, I thought it would be fitting to take a moment to remind us all about the power of unity.

Unity is defined by Merriam-Webster Dictionary as "the quality or state of being made one," wherein the "combination or ordering of the parts constitutes a whole or promotes an undivided total effect." Simply put, unity is a "condition of harmony" that is derived from our diversity. The word is derived from the Latin unitas or unus, which translates as "one." The unity concept is foundational to our nation's existence, so much so that it is emboldened in our country's name (the United States of America) and our original motto of a nation (E Pluribus Unum). I thought it might be fun to use today's segment to delve into this a bit more from a historical perspective.

Why are we called the "United" States of America? What does "E Pluribus Unum" even mean? How does this relate to Martin Luther King Jr.?

When the Second Continental Congress met in a sweltering hot Philadelphia in early July 1776, the delegates had had enough with King George III's draconian approach to rule. The King had repudiated the colonists' grievances that the various taxes levied upon them by the British Empire were harsh. Although the colonists initially differed in their opinions as to whether to separate from British rule, they finally reached an accord that secession was the only path forward. As a result, on July 2, 1776, the Second Continental Congress passed a unanimous resolution asserting independence. Two days later, Thomas Jefferson's Declaration of Independence was issued, proclaiming that the 13 colonies were now the United States of America. Interestingly, several other things happened on July 4, 1776, besides the issuance of the declaration. For one thing, a continental army was formed under General George Washington, since war had essentially been declared. Secondly, Congress began drafting a treaty with France and Spain to secure assistance in their fight against British Rule. Finally, on that same day, Congress voted to form a committee to design a seal for the new nation. That committee went off to work on the design, and, after about six weeks, they came up with an image of a shield with 13 smaller shields contained within it, surrounded by images of lady liberty, a continental soldier, and the eye of providence; this design bore a motto underneath it reading: "E Pluribus Unum." Well, as the years progressed, this seal was simplified to a bald eagle with a shield of 13 stripes on his breast, but the Latin motto remained. This new image became the official Great Seal of the United States, and the motto became an enduring fixture on our government documents, publications, and currency. In fact, it's interesting to learn that the first coins depicting a version of the 13-stripe seal and the motto of "E Pluribus Unum" were minted in no better place, than (drumroll please)...Rahway, New Jersey. The original New Jersey mint was situated along the Rahway River, about a few blocks from where the Merck Rahway facility currently resides. I'll come back to Rahway in a future *Thankful Thursday* segment. Until then, I'll point out to all our Merck Rahway colleagues that you can find a brick monument memorializing this event near the intersection of River Road and St. George Road, across from Rahway River Park. As someone who lived in Avenel, New Jersey, for some time, I know the area well.

So, what does this "E Pluribus Unum" motto mean?

"E Pluribus Unum" is a Latin phrase that translates to: "From many, one." It was specifically chosen for two reasons. First, the motto cleverly comprises 13 letters, which clearly carries symbolism pertaining to the 13 states that made up the original United States of America. Each letter is required to make the entire phrase work. More importantly, the motto epitomized the idea that the 13 states, which at that time made up this new nation of about 2.5 million individuals, were recognizably unique but they were choosing to come together to create a whole that was greater than the sum of its parts. Each state operated in its own way and espoused its own philosophies, but they came together under the auspices of a single nation governed by one Constitution. Now, I would be blowing smoke if I paint this all in a pretty light. The union was not perfect. Differences in culture, perspective, and philosophy, particularly as it pertained to the use of slave labor, would eventually boil up, culminating in a deadly five-year civil war about nine decades after the Declaration of Independence was signed. The nation has needed to adapt, as one can attest by the 27 amendments that have been added to the original Constitution—including one that ended slavery. Moreover, the country has needed to evolve from an agrarian society to a more industrial and technologically-focused one, especially as the national footprint has grown from the original 13 to the current 50 states.

As our small nation of 2.5 million individuals has grown to more than 350 million, our melting pot mentality has been challenged. Each and every one of us comes from a different upbringing. Our lack of familiarity with one another often poses a threat to many. Yet, it is that same diversity that has helped make the United States of America so innovative, so successful, and so desirable. Still, each and every day our nation struggles to remain unified and indivisible. The union is not perfect.

That's exactly the reason why today I'm thankful for all those who try to help us understand that we need to remain united to succeed. I am grateful for Martin Luther King Jr. I'm humbled by his steadfast commitment to the concept of unity, even though it would eventually lead to his own demise. We all know his 1963 "I Have a Dream" speech on the steps of the Lincoln Memorial and its reference to being "free at last," but the true message of integration, harmony, and concordance contained within that speech is often lost. We all need to work together to realize a world, a community, and a workplace where all individuals, irrespective of gender, race, ethnicity, sexual orientation, religious creed, or political philosophy, can come together for a common mission. Martin Luther King Jr. said many, many wonderful things, but there are three quotes I want to share with you because I think they truly espouse the concept of unity:

1. **"Love is the only force capable of transforming an enemy into a friend"[10]:** We are all fighting personal battles that others no nothing about. The only true way to overcome our differences is to approach each other with a spirit of understanding, compassion, and empathy. If we approach others with a sense of openness and appreciation of our differences, we are apt to find common ground upon which we can build stronger relationships.
2. **"We must all learn to live together as brothers or we will all perish together as fools"[11]:** I truly believe we all have good intent and want to live in a world or peace and harmony. We all also want to work for a company with a formidable and honorable purpose. Nevertheless, to reach these goals, we all need to work together in such a way that we respect, learn, and even embrace each other's differences.
3. **"We may have all come on different ships, but we're in the same boat now" [12]:** This quote is so poignant but so true. Whether we like it or not, we are all stuck with one another on this Earth, in this country, and in this office. The true superpowers we should possess are the fortitude, patience, and openness to work to advance our mission even in the face of our differences.

Merck is a very diverse company made up of nearly 70,000 employees from 140 different countries. Our Board of Directors and Executive Committee appreciate the complex task we all face in trying to bring together a workforce made up of diverse educational levels, disparate cultures, and unique viewpoints under a common mission and vision. As a company, we hope to embrace these differences to garner innovative thinking, much like the young United States has done as a nation.

One of the ways the company does this is through a focus on diversity and inclusion. I'm not sure if you are aware of this, but Merck has ten different Employee Business Resource Groups (EBRGs) with a focus on building diversity awareness and encouraging inclusion.

---

10 "Loving Your Enemies" speech delivered at the Dexter Avenue Baptist Church in Montgomery, AL, on Christmas Day, 1957.

11 "Remaining Awake Through a Great Revolution" Commencement Address delivered to Oberlin College, June 1965.

12 Origin unknown. The quote was repeated by Rep. John Lewis at the "Let Freedom Ring" ceremony, August 23, 2013, Washington DC.

These include the following; the Asia Pacific Association (APA), the Merck Rainbow Alliance (MRA), the Merck's Women Network (MWN), the Native American & Global Indigenous People, the Merck CapABILITY Network, the League of Employees of African Descent (LEAD), the Merck Hispanos Organization (MHO), the Merck Interfaith Organization, the Veterans Leadership Network (VLN), and the Next Gen Network (NGN).

Another way Merck and many other corporate or public entities embrace this arduous task is to use a team structure to get work done. Our Company leaders like to say that drug development is a team sport. Everything we do at Merck is based on a team structure, whether it is through our discovery and early development teams, our late development teams, and our various leadership/management teams. There's a reason for this. Research has repeatedly shown that a team will outperform the most capable member of a group, no matter what the scenario. To prove my point, I direct your attention to a hallmark study entitled "A Realistic Test of Individual Versus Group Consensus Decision Making" in the *Journal of Applied Psychology*, which was written by Larry Michealsen and others in 1989. In this trial, the authors collected data on 222 project teams, ranging from 3 to 8 members. What they found is not entirely surprising but, nevertheless, very striking: the group outperformed the most proficient member of each team 97 percent of the time. Moreover, over 40 percent of the process gains were synergistic; in other words, the benefits gained by the team could not be explained by the average score or the most knowledgeable group member's score. More so, the greatest gains occurred if the team members had the following four traits: competence, motivation, a commitment to continuous training, and diversity.

From my perspective, all four of those traits are critical, but I think it is fascinating to see that we need diversity to form our best teams. For sure, it is not easy to work in a highly-matrixed organization such as Merck, but it is really that sort of diversity, whether at the divisional level, departmental level, or individual level, that will help us challenge one other to produce the highest quality development strategies and execution plans. A survey conducted by *Forbes* back in 2011 of over 300 senior executives confirmed three interesting findings regarding diversity: (1) diversity is a key driver of a company's innovation and creativity; (2) a diverse workforce at a company helps attract top talent; and (3) the responsibility for the success of the company's diversity and inclusion efforts lies with its senior management. That makes it my responsibility and the responsibility of my peers.

So, as we approach the Martin Luther King Jr. holiday, let's embrace the diversity that each of us brings to the table for discussion and let's continually strive for common respect, inclusivity, and unity. Listen, it's never going to be perfect. Even after more than 240 years, the United States of America still struggles to meet the "E Pluribus Unum" motto. And even as a company, we are not there yet. There's room for improvement in the diversity area within my own group and at the higher echelons of the company. I commit to you that I will continue to do what I can to move a diversity mindset forward.

Of course, it isn't going to be easy. It isn't going to be solved immediately. It isn't going to be entirely what each of us might envision. All that said, it is the right thing to do. As Martin Luther King Jr. also once said, "The time is always right to do what is right."[13]

Let's face it. No matter where we come from, we're all in the same boat right now. We might as well stand united. E Pluribus Unum!

---

13 "Remaining Awake Through a Great Revolution" Commencement Address delivered to Oberlin College, June 1965.

10 Living in a Land Down Under *(January 31, 2019)*

For this week's *Thankful Thursday* segment, I am turning my gratitude southward towards a truly admirable, awe-inspiring place. Today, I pay my thanks to that large continent "Down Under" where Mad Max was conceived, marsupials run wild, and hot dogs are affectionately coined "tube steaks." Yes, my friends, my tribute this Thursday goes out to the great continent and island nation of Australia and all it has done to confront the scourge of infectious diseases.

As I awake this blistering cold, dark morning in late January, I am desperately longing for those long, hot days of summer. My nostalgia for those dog days of summer sitting on the beach in Martha's Vineyard leads to me ponder about life in Australia, where the Aussies have now officially embarked upon the summer season. Indeed, the official start of summer in Australia has taken place this week with the celebration of **Australia Day.** As the nation's official national holiday, Australia Day is celebrated annually on January 26, commemorating the arrival of the First Fleet of British ships into Australia and the raising of the flag of Great Britain in New South Wales in 1788. Although Australia had been discovered by the Dutch as New Holland nearly two centuries earlier, the country of The Netherlands never really claimed the land. The official claim to the land was made by British Lt. Captain James Cook, who first explored the eastern coast of Australia in 1770. However, the land would not be settled by the English for another two decades.

Why, you might ask?

Well, the British Empire really did not have a need for Australia. Whenever British folks got fed up with King George III's nonsense or that of any of his predecessors, they would simply emigrate to the various colonies in America. More so, it was common practice prior to the American Revolution for the Empire to send along its criminals and less than desirables to America. However, after the colonists chased the British away following the Battle of Yorktown in 1781, the British throne faced a dilemma: What on earth will we do with all the criminals we have in Great Britain? Then, someone remembered that an English Lt. Captain had claimed this large island in Oceania surrounded by the Indian and Pacific Oceans.

So, in May 1787, the British Empire sent the First Fleet of 11 ships from England to this new land with the intent of setting up a penal colony in the region where Cook had claimed British rule 17 years earlier. They finally arrived in January 1788 in Sydney Cove, in what is now Port Jackson. In addition to this original colony established in New South Wales, separate penal colonies would sprout up over the course of the next five decades in Tasmania as well as in what are now Queensland, Victoria, South Australia, and Western Australia. After many trials and tribulations, the practice of convict transportation would eventually cease in 1848. A few years later, population growth in Australia skyrocketed with a gold rush. In 1901, the federation of colonies, which included Queensland, New South Wales, Tasmania, Victoria, South Australia, and Western Australia, established the Commonwealth of Australia, commensurate to what we see today just north of us in Canada. In 1911 the Northern Territory separated from South Australia. Unfortunately, the original indigenous population, the Aborigines, would decline over this time, mostly due to infectious diseases brought by their invaders and forced assimilation. Today, Australia's population is about 25 million, of which less than 3 percent is Aboriginal.

Despite these somewhat inauspicious beginnings, Australia has grown to become one of the most lovable places on Earth. Now, for full disclosure, I must confess that I have never been to Australia, despite my strong interest in visiting the land of Oz. This is especially the case on a cold January day like today! Admittedly, I am sort of hoping that somehow my *Thankful Thursday* segment will make its way to some of our colleagues in MSD Australia, and an invitation will soon be forthcoming. Then, I could rightfully justify a trip to this Great Southern Land.

You might ask yourself why I possess so much love for Australia. How can someone be thankful for a place they've never visited?

First things first, everything I have ever read about this island continent has convinced me it is the closest thing to Nirvana that exists on this planet. Let's consider my rationale from the geographical, societal, and cultural perspective.

- From a geographical perspective, Australia is simply divine. We need to first start with the Great Barrier Reef, which is the world's longest coral reef, largest underwater living structure, and most diverse, living entity. The reef allows you to swim with an incredibly diverse array of creatures, from a clownfish like Nemo to sea turtles like Crush and even certain variety of sharks like Bruce and Anchor. Australia also boasts 500 national parks, multiple rainforests, and the world's largest number of beaches. I read this interesting statistic recently: if one ventured on a daily beach trek to every Australian beach, it would take 27 years to see them all. More so, over 80 percent of their plants, mammals, and in-shore fish and 45 percent of the birds are native to Australia. Unique critters, such as kangaroos, koalas, platypuses, and wombats, roam aplenty in the dry, temperate regions, where they eat the lush eucalyptus trees among other foliage and jump on or crawl over incredible sandstone rock formations.
- From a societal perspective, Australian people rank high in cordiality and are cheerful, happy-go-lucky chaps. Who wouldn't be happy to live in a democratic country with one of the most progressive set of civil, political, and economic liberties? Australia also holds claim to four of the top ten most livable cities in the world, including Melbourne at #1, and the third highest life expectancy. Economically speaking, Australia is the wealthiest nation in the world. Notably, it's the only place where a recession did not take hold in the last decade, and, in fact, this country is the newly-anointed leader in the world's Human Development Index, having recently surpassed Norway this past year for the top spot. They've never had a civil war, 99 percent of their population is literate, and over 90 percent of the people vote. That's what happens when you mandate that people submit a ballot, even if it's blank, and when you hold elections on a Saturday as opposed to a Tuesday. What a concept!

- Finally, from a cultural perspective, Australians have a zest for life. They love their disparate music tastes, their many sports, and their food. You can go from listening to "Back in Black" by AC/DC to "I'm All Out of Love" by Air Supply in the blink of an eye. If you prefer, you can take in a symphonic orchestra at the Sydney Opera House. Aussies love their cricket, golf, basketball, tennis, water-based sports, and, of course, Australian rules football. When ESPN first aired, when the programming was a bit slim, I got really into Australian Rules Football, a civilized sport played on an oval-shaped field. In what other sport do you find referees wearing suits, ties, and brimmed hats? On the basketball front, I'm also thankful for Ben Simmons, their favorite NBA son, who will one day, with the help of a few other immigrants, restore glory to the Philadelphia 76ers franchise. Finally, their idea of a splendid meal is a plentiful barbie, wherein one scarfs down red meat, drinks a few coldies, and still saves some space for pavlova and lamingtons. As a carnivore, I must admit that sounds pretty awesome.

Yes, Australia seems to be heaven on earth.

But the true reason I laud the sunburnt country of Australia and have chosen to pay tribute to this nation this morning is tied to their medical practice of infectious diseases. Australia has one of the highest functioning health care systems in the world, and, frankly, they seem to put their healthcare dollars, which account for only about nine percent of their total gross domestic product, to excellent use. As opposed to maintaining a siloed therapeutic-only methodology to healthcare expenditure, they routinely focus their efforts on disease prevention, behavior modification, and public health initiatives. The Australians never shy away from a medical challenge. Just in the last six months, I've come across at least four different publications in the infectious disease literature to prove my point. These manuscripts highlight Australia's incredible strides in helping to vaccinate adolescents with the 9-valent vaccine against human papilloma virus, expand treatment coverage for those with chronic Hepatic C virus (HCV) infection, implement pre-exposure prophylaxis (PrEP) to prevent acquisition of HIV infection in high-risk patient populations, and improve infection control measures to prevent bacterial infections in the hospital setting. You can read my synopsis of each of these four articles in **Table 1**.

In short, I hope my essay has proven to you why Australia rocks far beyond the melodies of AC/DC, Men at Work, Midnight Oil, and the Little River Band. They seem to make a commitment to something, especially in the public health arena, and then follow through on those commitments. In turn, good things start to happen. Many of the world's governments, healthcare institutions, and medical policy makers may want to book a flight, grab some paper and a pencil, and head Down Under to see if they can a lesson from these progressive Aussies.

Now listen, I'm not so naïve as to think that everything about Australia is peachy-keen and copasetic. They have their share of issues and problems. For one thing, they have the highest rate of skin cancer in the world. Their population is growing older, they imbibe alcohol to an eye-popping level, and their mean body mass index (BMI) is not something to write home about. They have some the world's highest carbon dioxide emissions, despite repeated efforts to curb their carbon footprint through national use taxes. Australia also possesses some down-right scary creatures. Folks routinely posts frightening stories on Facebook about some Australian household waking up to find a 16-foot python hiding in the cupboard beneath their kitchen sink or a 12-foot crocodile sunning itself by the pool. Some have even claimed that the dingos can eat their babies. I would also add that, on occasion, I have no idea what an Australian is saying. During my medical residency, one of my good Australian friends would never say "Yes" or "OK" to a question. Instead, it was always "No worries" or "No drama," or my all-time favorite, "Too easy." Finally, as proof that not all things in Australia are rational, I offer up vegemite. What the heck is the point to vegemite? Why ruin a good barbie with such a bad idea?

All that said, Australia is, in my estimation, downright awesome, and I am thankful for all it has taught me about infectious disease and living life to the fullest.

Now, I just need to figure out which colleague to send this to at our company's Australian subsidiary, MSD Australia, so I can secure my invitation and plan my trip to visit those living in a land Down Under.

Table 1. Four Recent Articles Highlighting Australia's Progressive Public Health Efforts

1. First, let's start with an interesting article pertaining to the 9-valent vaccine against human papillomavirus (HPV). The uptake of HPV vaccination in Australia, where the national government has wholeheartedly embraced vaccination and HPV screening, has been outstanding. In October of last year, *Lancet* published an interesting article that predicted scenarios for Australia's elimination of cervical cancer. Based on current modeling estimates, Australia is on track to eliminate cervical cancer as a public health problem by 2028. (Click on the following link to learn more: https://www.thelancet.com/journals/lanpub/article/PIIS2468-2667(18)30183-X/fulltext)
2. But, it is not just cervical cancer that they are working to eliminate. I recently came across an article in the *Journal of Viral Hepatitis,* published in September 2018, wherein the authors modelled Australia's ability to eliminate chronic Hepatic C virus (HCV) infection. Like HPV vaccination, subsidized direct-acting antiviral (DAA) treatment has recently become available to all adults living with chronic HCV in Australia. Based on rapid uptake of nearly 33,000 subjects who initiated DAAs in 2016 alone, these authors estimate Australia is on track to meet the World Health Organization (WHO) targets of HCV incidence reduction by 2028. Looks like 2028 is setting up to become a banner year for the Land Down Under. (Click on the following link to learn more: https://onlinelibrary.wiley.com/doi/full/10.1111/jvh.13013)
3. But, HPV and HCV are not the only viruses Australians want to curb. An article that was published in *Lancet HIV* last October describes the incredible effort of rapid implementation of pre-exposure prophylaxis (PrEP) against HIV infection in high-risk men-having-sex-with-men (MSM) in New South Wales, Australia's most populous state. The researchers conducted an implementation cohort study of daily co-formulated tenofovir disoproxil fumarate (TDF) and emtricitabine (FTC) as HIV PrEP. Their results show that HIV diagnoses in MSM in New South Wales declined from 295 in the 12 months before the PrEP roll-out to 221 in the 12 months after the PrEP roll-out (relative risk reduction (RRR) 25.1%; 95% CI 10.5–37.4). The study confirmed what was expected: PrEP implementation can be associated with a rapid decline in HIV

diagnoses across a large geographic region. (Click on the following link to learn more: https://www.thelancet.com/journals/lanhiv/article/PIIS2352-3018(18)30215-7/fulltext)

4. But all this prior work is focused entirely on viruses. Can Australians also prevent bacterial infections? Of course, they can, and a recent journal article in the November 2018 edition of *Lancet Infectious Diseases* confirms this point. The article reports on the nation-wide Australian campaign to promote hand hygiene compliance, a program that has been in place for nearly ten years. Following the 2009 publication of the WHO guidelines for hand hygiene, Australians embedded these guidelines into the national system for accrediting private and public hospitals. The authors of this journal article highlight how such sanitizing practices have allowed Australia to become the first country to show a robust association between handwashing and a lowered incidence of *Staphylococcus aureus* bacteremia. Year-on-year hand compliance in Australia has increased since the program was instituted in 2009, with a corresponding decrease in *S. aureus* bacteremia. (Click on the following link to learn more: https://www.thelancet.com/journals/laninf/article/PIIS1473-3099(18)30491-2/fulltext

11 St. Valentine and the Virtuous Cycle *(February 14, 2019)*

For this week's *Thankful Thursday* segment, I wanted to take the opportunity to express my appreciation for those who pay it forward and prosper in return because of their own benevolence. In other words, I am thankful for the "virtuous cycle."

First things first: Happy Valentine's Day to each of you.

I do sincerely hope you are fortunate enough to receive one or more of the nearly 200 million Valentine Day cards that have been created by the Greeting Card industry for this year's event. Astoundingly, this absurd number approaches 1 billion if one includes all the Valentine cards created and exchanged today in US schools, daycare centers, and retirement homes. Over 225 million roses have been pruned for this year's holiday, and more than 58 million pounds of chocolate will be shared with loved ones. If you aspire to gender equality, you might be dismayed to discover that 85 percent of all Valentine's Day cards are purchased by women, while nearly 73 percent of all flowers are purchased by men. Fortunately, you'll be less horrified to learn that chocolate and candy are equitably purchased by the two sexes. In sum, over $20 billion will be spent this Valentine's Day on cards and gifts, including a whopping $4.5 billion on jewelry and an eye-opening $680 million on gifts for our pets. (Rightfully so, dogs usually make out better than cats on this holiday. I'll explain my love for canines in a few months' time.) Hopefully, you have already booked your dinner reservation; otherwise, you will be sorely disappointed, as today is the second busiest day of the year for restauranteurs.

I became a bit flabbergasted by these figures, and my mind started wondering as to how this Hallmark holiday even came into being. So, as a learned scientist, I did what I do best: I conducted some research to uncover the history behind this event. Sadly, the story behind the Valentine's Day celebration and the patron saint for whom it is named, St. Valentine, is not as clear-cut as the account of St. Nicholas of Myra, which I shared in a *Thankful Thursday* segment in early December. I came across three separate martyrs named Valentine who are now each venerated as a saint. So, instead of boring you with each account, I decided to share the version I found most intriguing.

According to an ancient legend, one of the St. Valentines was a Roman priest who lived in the third century during the dictatorial reign of Claudius II. Supposedly, the Roman Emperor came to the conclusion that single men made more valiant soldiers than married men, so he outlawed the marriage of young men. However, Valentine condemned this decree as both unjust and immoral, opting to perform the marriages of young lovers in secret. Unfortunately, his clandestine act was revealed, and Valentine was persecuted and eventually killed for his transgression in 279 AD. Valentine was subsequently canonized in 496, and his celebration was added to the calendar of saints on February 14. This day was specifically chosen to coincide with a pagan festival called Lupercalia, which had been celebrated on the Ides of February (February 13-15). Lupercalia was a fertility festival dedicated to the two Roman founding brothers, Romulus and Remus. According to Roman lore, these two infants were raised by a she-wolf. In commemoration of the holiday, dogs and goats were sacrificed and their hides were paraded through the streets of Rome; women would then touch the bloodied hides in the hope that it would improve their fertility in the coming year. Later in the day, unmarried Roman women would write their names on cards and add the cards to an urn. The eligible bachelors of Rome would choose a card and be paired with the named woman for the coming year. Not surprisingly, the Church heavily disapproved of this festival, so it decided to Christianize the pagan festival and replace it with St. Valentine's Day.

However, the legend of St. Valentine's support for love, coupled with the pagan festivities, set the stage for having Valentine's Day recognized as a cultural celebration of romance and love. The religious celebration gained momentum through the Middle Ages, at which time the heart emerged as a symbolic portrayal of steadfast love and commitment. By the fifteenth century, the creation of poetry and hand-written letters to loved ones, often adorned with a heart, were popularized in England. Shakespeare added to the momentum; he paid proper homage to the holiday in *Hamlet* in 1600, and, his sonnets were a quintessential tribute to the mysteries of human love. By the nineteenth century, hand-written Valentine cards with messages of love gave way to the mass production of Valentine's cards. And the rest is history.

I thought today's celebration would be a fine occasion to discuss love in the context of our work here at Merck. Many have written on the meaning of love as an emotion shared between two individuals, but the definition that resonates with me comes from the 1916 novel In the *Garden of Delights*. In the novel, the author Lily Hardy Hammond put it best: "You don't pay love back; you pay it forward." With this in mind, I gravitate to the concept of the virtuous cycle. We all know about a vicious cycle, as it is a fixture of the modern lexicon. In fact, we all can come up with instances of such vicious occurrences. Examples include the compounding interest on a credit card or the spread of bubonic plague in a crowded, impoverished region. Nonetheless, I think a virtuous cycle deserves its fair share of acknowledgment. In brief, a virtuous cycle is a complex chain of positive events that are perpetuated through a positive feedback loop.

Case in point is the heart itself, a fitting example for today's *Thankful Thursday* theme. In addition to serving as the popular symbol for this holiday, the heart's other primary role is to pump blood to the entire body, bringing oxygen from the lungs to all organs, including the heart and lungs; in turn, the lungs are energized to continue gathering oxygen and the heart continues to pump this newly acquired oxygen to meet the needs of all organs. As old cells die away, the oxygen that is provided back to the lungs and heart helps to produce energy that leads to the growth of new heart cells (myocytes) or lung cells (pulmonary alveoli). In turn, these organs continue to perform their functions in perfect harmony and the positive feedback loop is maintained.

But what I believe is even more fascinating is that virtuous cycles can be found all around us in our daily work.

Take for instance our business model for the pharmaceutical industry, which is essentially a virtuous cycle. Simply put, our company works on the concept that once a Merck-derived innovative product, such as the 9-valent human papillomavirus vaccine, the antibiotic imipenem, or the cancer agent pembrolizumab, is licensed, it will be first and foremost be used to assist those patients in need. In turn, a cash flow from the sale of the products will be generated that allows our company to reinvest in discovery research to develop more innovative products, such as new mechanisms against cancer, bacterial infections, or other pathogens that could serve as vaccine targets. As those new products are discovered, developed, and eventually licensed for use, either alone or in combination with other existing products, more individuals in need benefit. Thus, further revenues are generated to support the continued replenishment of the research and development budget. In turn, the cycle of scientific discovery is positively reinforced. Merck understands this cycle and chooses as its fundamental, core mission to let science dictate our path forward, not mergers and acquisitions. It is my humble belief that a pharmaceutical industry that attempts to grow through large acquisitions will ultimately fail if those revenues are not funneled back into research and development.

Another interesting virtuous cycle is the concept of global immunization. I'll highlight an example from the Global Polio Eradication Initiative (GPEI) to prove my point. As many of you know, polio is a debilitating, incurable disease caused by an enterovirus. Less than four decades ago, polio paralyzed about 300,000 children a year, at a rate of over 800 new cases per day, essentially 40 per hour. Thanks to the efforts of the GPEI, a public-private enterprise, over 20 million volunteers have attempted to eradicate this scourge from the earth. The case for polio eradication, like most vaccination efforts, is a virtuous cycle. First, a child is vaccinated against polio or another disease. This immunization leads to better health overall at the individual level. Fortuitously, vaccination also improves health at the population level through herd immunity, thereby further reducing the number of new polio cases. Better health outcomes ultimately result in lower costs for a family or community, who then can use their resources for other needs. The physical and emotional mindset of a family or community is strengthened, children are capable of attending schools and gaining economic opportunities, and healthcare resources at the family and community level can be appropriately allocated to other venues of medical necessity. Ultimately, this results in productivity gains for local, regional, and national economies. All the while, the disease's prevalence is gradually reduced to a point of near eradication. As we start 2019, we now sit on the cusp of polio eradication. As a result of over 2.5 billion child vaccinations via the GPEI efforts over the last 40 years, 16 million more people are walking today, more than $27 billion in healthcare savings have been realized, including another $17 billion in nutritional-related services, and the total number of new cases of polio has been drastically reduced to about 40 per year, in contrast to 40 per hour.

Notably, many of the global vaccine networks also work through a virtuous cycle. Take, for example, the Global Alliance for Vaccines and Immunization (GAVI), a global effort to bring life-saving vaccines to children in lower income countries. GAVI is founded on the principle that as greater immunization coverage is implemented in a country, the population becomes more productive and achieves greater prosperity; in turn, countries are able to pay for their vaccines and transition out of the program. Perhaps it is best to compare it to the boats in a marina: it's inspiring to lift up one boat, but if you raise the tide, you can lift all the boats simultaneously.

I'd also like to share an interesting Merck story of a virtuous cycle. Our former CEO, Roy Vagelos was born and raised in Rahway, New Jersey. As a child, he worked at his parent's luncheonette in downtown Rahway, where he often catered to and learned from Merck-employed chemists, engineers, and scientists; in turn, they inspired him to pursue a career in medicine. After achieving his medical degree and a successful academic career in lipid research at Washington University in St. Louis and at Columbia University, Roy brought his learnings back to Merck, in his hometown of Rahway, where he helped propagate a first-in-class hyperlipidemia agent, the statin lovastatin. The global impact from statin therapy has been enormous. But, the story does not end there. Roy was eventually promoted from Head of MRL to CEO at Merck, where he witnessed firsthand the incredible research and development efforts that Drs. William Campbell and Mohammed Aziz led for our anti-infective agent, ivermectin. Roy recognized the drug had its greatest value in treating parasitic infections, such as river blindness (onchocerciasis), in the developing world. Many leaders, including former President Jimmy Carter, encouraged Roy to identify a means by which to distribute ivermectin (MECTIZAN®) free of charge to those who needed it most. So in 1987, a year when both lovastatin and MECTIZAN® were formally approved, Roy announced that Merck would provide ivermectin, as much as needed for as long as needed, through the MECTIZAN® Donation Program (MDP). To facilitate drug distribution, Merck partnered with the Carter Center, the philanthropic organization founded in Atlanta by President Carter after his term in the White House ended in 1980, to help distribute MECTIZAN®. To this day, the MDP partnership with the Carter Center remains intact, and Merck plans to support the MDP into perpetuity until onchocerciasis is effectively eliminated from the world (**Figure 6**). But the story does not end there either. The important work that President Carter did with Merck for the world would pay itself forward. A few years ago, President Carter was diagnosed with Stage IV melanoma with brain metastases. As good fortune would have it, President Carter was treated with Merck's pembrolizumab. His tumors eventually regressed, thereby allowing him to continue to shepherd the great work of the Carter Center, including its role in the MDP. The virtuous cycle keeps giving!

I started my *Thankful Thursday* initiative last year with the hope that I could inspire my teams through stories of gratitude and appreciation. Selfishly, I've also used these segments as a means to strengthen my own writing skills so that when I retire, I'll be more equipped to pursue my second career as an author. Unexpectedly, I have discovered that each segment I finish reenergizes me to write a new segment. More amazingly if not ironically, the positive feedback and enthusiastic appreciation I've received from each of you serves as an impetus to keep the tradition going. So, I guess you can say that a virtuous cycle has been born.

In closing, I'm thankful today to all those who have taught us the power of paying it forward. Sometimes random acts of kindness have a way of perpetuating themselves into fortuitous actions. In turn, these actions result in a betterment of science, our industry, and humanity, eventually resulting in the creation of a virtuous cycle. We'll come back to the theme of kindness and generosity in a future *Thankful Thursday* segment.

So as you sit there today eating a chocolate praline from one of the 36 billion heart-shaped boxes that will be sold today, take a second to think about how you might be able to pay it forward to someone in need. Maybe it's just a kind email note to your direct report or a sonnet to a loved one. For your convenience, I'm sending along a site where you can find one of 18 different Valentine email templates you can use (https://blog.sendblaster.com/2014/01/27/10-free-valentines-day-email-templates-for-sendblaster) and a site that teaches you how to write a Valentine sonnet (https://www.surfnetkids.com/valentinesday/1164/why-and-how-to-write-a-love-sonnet). Better yet, you can send a Valentine's Day card attached with one of the eight billion Sweetheart Conversation Hearts that have been mass produced by the Necco Candy company for the occasion, perhaps with the phrase "Smile," "TXT Me," or "Wicked Cool".

Whatever you choose to do, I hope you have fun, and Happy Valentine's Day to you!

12 A Man for Our Times
(February 21, 2019)

For this week's *Thankful Thursday* segment, I am taking the liberty of lauding my favorite Greek guide, mentor, and old friend. I share my admiration of the world's first moral philosopher, and, in turn, express my profound gratitude for the lessons he has taught me about science, leadership, and life.

This past week, I had the pleasure to travel to the motherland—Greece—to help support the European launch of doravirine, the non-nucleoside reverse transcriptase inhibitor (NNRTI). Doravirine is a new treatment for patients living with HIV. As I am writing this segment, I'm travelling back home, flying 36,000 feet over the Atlantic Ocean, contemplating my extended Greek family, whom I was ecstatic to visit while in Greece's capital city, Athens. As I sit in my seat, my mind wanders to my ancient Greek idol, and I ponder over the life he led and the legacy he left behind. In case you have not figured it out yet, my idol is none other than Socrates—the moral philosopher, not the center back for the Arsenal Club in the Premier League, nor the midfielder of the 1982 Brazilian World Cup team.

I need to start by telling you a secret. I have a huge crush on Socrates. Although I've never met him, as no time machines exist to transport me back 2,500 years, I feel I have a special connection to him. In short, there are three reasons why I harbor such an ardent attachment to this mysterious individual:

1. **My Love of the Socratic Method**: Socrates embodied the belief that the best way to understand an issue is through detailed

examination. Through a series of inquiries, he hoped to glean knowledge about a specific topic and, if necessary, help the ones responding to his queries recognize the error in their thinking. Socrates' method of questioning, known as dialectic, forms the foundation of our modern legal system, our pursuit of scientific knowledge, and, of course, the delicate art of parenting teenagers. I'll come back to the Socratic Method in just a second.

2. **An Ancestral Brethren**: My brother, Phil, recently completed a 23 and Me® blood test to trace his ancestral roots. Not surprisingly, he is 94 percent Greek—the other 6 percent was Turkish, I think. As my brother and I presumably come from the same parents, I can safely deduce my genetic makeup is the same as his. My predominantly Greek heritage gives me a glimmer of hope that Socrates might indeed be a long-lost relative, from whom I've inherited some genetic elements.
3. **The Father of Three Sons**: I was thrilled to uncover a silly tidbit about Socrates' life. Socrates, like me, fathered three sons. As someone who is reminded nightly by my offspring as to how poorly versed I am in politics, sports, world events, and even medicine, I'm comforted knowing that Socrates must have encountered similar treatment in his own household. Why else would Socrates walk the streets of Athens, proclaiming: "I know nothing except for the fact of my ignorance?"

Socrates never wrote anything down in his lifetime, and he never gave a public address. Sadly, our knowledge of this great man rests wholly on the input of a few of his contemporary colleagues, including his students Plato and Xenophon and the playwright Aristophanes, who made his living mocking most Athenians. Even worse, some of the writings we have from Plato cannot be fully trusted, as Plato often used Socrates as a voice for his own perspectives on philosophical topics, such as courage, justice, and virtue. Collectively, scholars and biographers have pieced together an account of the man and his life based on the most reliable data we have from the time.

What we know is the following: Socrates was born in 470 BC into a middle-class family living in Ancient Greece. He lived his entire life within the confines of the city-state of Athens at its heyday of wealth, culture, and growth. This era was called The Golden Age of Greece. In his early life, he supposedly followed his father's path and worked as a mason. He even fought valiantly in several battles in the armored infantry (the Hoplite), but he never maintained a real occupation. He chose the life as a sophist, an individual who would spend time educating the upper-class youth of Athens. He often did so in the Greek marketplace at the foot of the Acropolis, known as the Agora of Athens. He never accepted financial remuneration for his sophist work, choosing to remain destitute. However, his gregarious personality, authentic style, and genial gift for gab won him many friends, and, hence, he was never in wont of food, shelter, or entertainment. He wore ragged cloaks, always walked barefoot, and never cared for his physical appearance; in fact, he had been repeatedly mocked as the "ugliest" man to walk the streets of Athens. Nonetheless, he exercised regularly and maintained a steadfast belief that all things were best consumed or enjoyed in moderation. In turn, he lived to the ripe age of 70 years, and would likely have endured into his 80s or 90s if he had not been sentenced to death in 399 BC for the crimes of sedition—corruption of the youth—and harboring religious beliefs not aligned with those of the Greek populace.

What makes Socrates so memorable was both his philosophical beliefs and his approach to attaining knowledge. His philosophical premise was that knowledge was acquired to improve the greater well-being of society. Essentially, individuals should use human reasoning, as opposed to some civic or societal doctrine, to achieve virtue—true happiness—in life. In other words, a person needed to reflect internally to arrive at his own set of truths regarding everything from law and justice to abstract topics such as morality, ethics, and courage. His personal steadfast belief was that virtue could be derived only from doing good, and one could never waver from this belief. This moral absolutism would form the basis of modern Western philosophy and our current legal system. As he was known to say on endless occasions, "un unexamined life is not worth living." With this guiding principle, he walked the streets of Athens asking questions in a polite, non-threatening way to all, including the elite ruling class, the aristocrats, the great playwrights, artists, historians, the middle class, and even slaves, with the goal of seeking truth. He spent many hours hobnobbing at the Athenian symposia with such great men as Euripides, Sophocles, Aristophanes, and Pericles. His dialectic methodology was not intended to teach Athenians what to think, but rather how to think.

I bring up Socrates today because he reminds me of what we are striving to do here at Merck. Our company strategy is simple: We follow the science to discover, develop, and bring to market innovative human and animal health medicines, vaccines, and solutions that address significant unmet medical needs and deliver patient and customer value. But how we do it also matters. I'll use three learnings from Socrates to highlight my point.

First, we remain steadfast in our pursuit of scientific inquiry and discovery. Socrates never wavered from his belief that all knowledge, whether scientific or philosophical in nature, comes from asking questions, and as answers are gleaned to those inquiries, further questions should follow to fine tune one's viewpoint of a topic at hand. He also believed that knowledge was asymptotic; that is, one could get close to the truth but never fully understand all the intricacies associated with it. It is for this reason Socrates proclaimed to be ignorant and yet still wise, as he readily accepted his imperfections and fallibility. The same is true with our work in Merck Research Laboratories (MRL). We perform experiments, whether it be in vitro studies, in vivo experiments, or even clinical trials in human participants, with the humble intent of acquiring knowledge about a disease, a drug product, or a development process. In the world of late stage development, we design clinical trials to answer questions; our studies are not sufficiently powered to do more than just that. And, as we obtain data or knowledge from a single trial, it catapults us forward to ask new questions and perform new studies. As many of you are fully aware, most of our studies are designed to answer one or two pre-defined hypotheses; everything else we glean generates a new hypothesis that then requires confirmation. As Socrates never ceased in his pursuit of knowledge, so we should never cease in our pursuit of new scientific knowledge.

Second, as we perform our work, we need to maintain laser-focused on maintaining high-quality conversations with our colleagues, whether it be our team members, direct reports, or the external scientific community. Socrates' barrage of questions was not just a vehicle for friendly socialization but also an implement to force his responder to earnestly deliberate as to the true meaning of the question. Essentially, his aim was to force robust debate and discussion on a difficult issue and generate insight to a complicated topic. Although many Athenians found his unique approach to be bit obscure and at times exhausting, he always did so in a professional, congenial, and non-threatening way. Socrates was never offensive nor off-putting. In **Table 2**, I've included a brief version of a fun exchange between Socrates and one of his colleagues, Critobulus, regarding his own acknowledgment of his ugly countenance. I'm sharing this Beauty Contest debate just to prove how these exchanges were both insightful and humorous at the same time. A member of our Human Resources department recently sent me a fascinating article in the *Neuro Leadership Journal* that speaks to the power of insights about ourselves. Internal aha moments are extremely powerful, leading to enhanced learning, active engagement, and broader generalization; such insights can even lead to systemic, long-lasting changes in the brain. We should all help our colleagues achieve such heights through high-quality discussions, irrespective of the situation. Whether it is a clinical director discussing a complex analysis with a statistician, a development team leader problem-solving with a manufacturing lead, or a manager discussing stakeholder feedback with a direct report, I encourage you to approach each conversation in a thoughtful, direct manner. Such high-quality conservations are apt to engender greater insights and possibly some innovative solutions. This idea of insight should not seem novel or entirely foreign to us. In fact, insight is the impetus that propelled Socrates' most famous pupil, Plato, to open the Academy, the first university of higher learning in the Western world.

Finally, we need to approach all our daily interactions with candor and courage. In my estimation, Socrates may have been the bravest man to ever live. I mentioned before that he was regarded as one of the most valiant soldiers in the Greek infantry; however, I found it even more fascinating to learn that he saved the life of a popular Athenian general, Alcibiades, at the Battle of Potidaea, by standing over his wounded body during an intense moment of hand-to-hand combat. Later in his life, after Athens had lost the Peloponnesian War to the Spartans, Socrates demonstrated courage again when he was commanded in 404 BC by the Oligarchy of 30 Tyrants, who ruled Greece in the war's aftermath, to go to Greek island of Salamis and retrieve an Athenian deserter to stand trial for treason. Socrates flatly refused, informing the rulers that such a request was unjust and immoral. He went home instead. Finally, a few years later, he made the ultimate sacrifice. With Athens in disarray and in reflective doubt over how it had mightily fallen after the Peloponnesian War, many Athenian dignitaries blamed the sophists such as Socrates for recklessly leading the once-revered city-state to its downfall. Of course, this was not true at all. As a scapegoat, Socrates stood trial, lost, and was condemned to death. As he lay in his jail cell awaiting the arrival of the poison hemlock that would lead to his demise, his friends successfully bribed a prison guard so that Socrates could readily escape into exile (**Figure 7**). However, Socrates refused to leave, claiming this was not the moral thing to do and would fly in the face of all his ethical principles and philosophical tenets.

How does this all relate to your daily roles? Let's be clear: I'm not asking you to drink hemlock; however, I do encourage you to act with courage and candor in your daily interactions, speaking your mind in a thoughtful, respectful manner.

Socrates knew that all humans are imperfect; thus, striving for a virtuous existence requires constant self-assessment in one's daily life. He also recognized that personal improvement requires a willingness to accept feedback. After Aristophanes produced the play *Clouds*, a parody mocking the sophists such as Socrates, one of Socrates' trusted friend, Alcibiades, asked Socrates if he was offended by the performance. His response is classic (no pun intended): "If what they say is true, I must continue to work to do better. But, if it isn't, then it really does not matter."

So, today, I am thankful for this great philosopher and the father of modern Western thought. I'm grateful for all Socrates has taught me, albeit indirectly from the writings of others, about the important things in life: friendship, community, and the pursuit of virtue. His lessons in humility have helped me at work, at home, and at play. He's also taught me that invoking some playfulness and laughter, even at work, is totally fine; indeed, Socrates was the first to use humor as a wonderful, disarming tool. Most importantly, he taught me not to take myself so damn seriously.

So, as my flight from Athens approaches Newark, I say *Eucaristo*, or thank you, to my Greek friend and confidante. I might not know much, at least according to my kids, but least I'm wise enough to know that it really does not matter what they think.

P.S. In case you are interested, the best biography I've ever read on Socrates was written by the British historian Paul Johnson and is entitled *Socrates: A Man for Our Times*. It's a quick read and extremely entertaining. I highly recommend it.

Table 2. Socrates and the Beauty Contest

As the story goes, Socrates challenged Critobulus, a handsome young Athenian man, to a beauty contest as a joke, especially since Socrates knew he was not attractive.

Socrates: Why Critobulus do you flaunt your looks as if you were more handsome than me?
Critobulus: Oh, I know I'm inferior to you in beauty, Socrates; therefore, I must be even uglier than the half-human satyr, Silenus.
Socrates: Are only men handsome?
Critobulus: No, a horse or a bull can be handsome, even a shield.
Socrates: How is it that such different things could all be handsome?
Critobulus: Because they are well made by art or by nature for their purpose.
Socrates: What are eyes for?
Critobulus: To see.
Socrates: For that reason, my eyes are more handsome than yours.
Critobulus: How so?
Socrates: Yours can see only a different line, but mine can do that and see sideways too because they stick out so much. And is your nose better shaped than mine?
Critobulus: Yes.
Socrates: If God made the nose for smelling, your nostrils are inefficiently turned down, while mine are turned up and can receive smells from every direction.
Critobulus: I grant you your mouth is better, for if God gave us mouths to eat, yours is big enough to gobble three times as much as mine.
Socrates: Yes, and my kisses are sweeter and more luscious than yours since my lips are so big and thick.

Adapted from Xenophon's *Symposium* and beautifully summarized by Paul Johnson in *Socrates: A Man for Our Times*. By the way, when the votes of all those at the Symposium were collected and counted, Critobulus won the contest unanimously.

13 A Solemn Salute to Serendipity *(March 7, 2019)*

For this week's *Thankful Thursday* segment, I'd like to marvel a bit about all those pleasant, unanticipated discoveries that have helped facilitate our comprehension of infectious diseases. These fortunate surprises have advanced global health, and, in turn, all of humankind have reaped their benefits. Please stand and salute, as I sing a song for scientific serendipity!

Two things have occurred this week that now lead me to contemplate the topic at hand:

- First, many of our colleagues on the human immunodeficiency virus (HIV) teams are currently gathered in the lovely Emerald City—also known as Seattle—to attend this year's Conference on Retroviruses and Opportunistic Infections (CROI). CROI is one of the preeminent scientific conferences held annually to discuss, debate, and disseminate emerging data on HIV. This year, our stellar HIV teams will be presenting data on multiple products in Merck's HIV portfolio, including raltegravir, doravirine, and, of course, MK-8591. I'll come back to MK-8591 in just a moment.
- Second, an interesting song shuffled through my Apple Music playlist on my ride home, and it sparked my thinking about my favorable accidents. Recently, as part of my evening commutes, I've been listening a lot to my Apple Music playlist. This is partly because National Public Radio (NPR) has recently embarked on one of their never-ending, excruciating pledge drives. When this happens, my immediate back-up plan is to listen to Sports

> Talk Radio, but lately that too has been equally insufferable. So, Back-up Option #2 for the ride home is Apple Music. Now, when I started the *Thankful Thursday* segment a while back, one stipulation I told myself that I would heed was to never overshare personal information in these segments. So, I'm going to break my own rule for just a millisecond and share with you an inner feature of my life—the details surrounding my Apple Music playlist. I like to think that my taste in music is very eclectic; it is commonplace for my ride home to be filled with songs from the Beatles (anything from *St. Pepper's Lonely Hearts Club Band*), musical medleys from *Hamilton* (as you'd might expect from a prior segment), and an occasional hit from bands like Metallica, Rush, Eminem, Katy Perry, Queen, or Sheryl Crow. On Monday's ride home, Sheryl Crow's "My Favorite Mistake" shuffled through, and it got me thinking about life, science, and some of my favorite mistakes.

These two simultaneous occurrences then conjured up memories of the discovery of MK-8591. MK-8591 is our novel investigational agent[14] to treat HIV. As a nucleoside reverse transcriptase translocation inhibitor (NRTTI), MK-8591 has demonstrated some compelling properties, including robust potency, a high genetic barrier to resistance development, an extremely long half-life, and the intriguing ability to penetrate HIV latent reservoirs, such as lymphoid tissue in the intestine or in reproductive organs. Altogether, these properties suggest that MK-8591 could have a drastic effect on HIV virus levels in the blood (or viremia) with an extremely low dose administered over a relatively prolonged interval. In fact, if our early clinical studies hold true, the MK-8591 dose needed to treat HIV infection might be as little as less than one milligram per day. That's awfully impressive for an antiviral agent. Several HIV teams are currently propagating MK-8591 through various stages of preclinical and clinical development, with our lead program focused on a single, once-daily regimen combining MK-8591 with another Merck HIV agent, doravirine (MK-8591A). Other teams are exploring its role as a long-acting agent, in either oral or implantable form, for treatment or pre-exposure prophylaxis (PrEP) against HIV. So far, the data on this NRTTI, albeit still in the early phases of development, has been impressive. MK-8591 not only has the potential to revolutionize how we treat HIV infection in people

14 A substance that has been tested in the laboratory and has been approved by the U.S. Food and Drug Administration for testing in people.

living with HIV, but it could also play a crucial role in preventing the transmission of HIV if used as a PrEP in those individuals at high risk of acquiring HIV.

The story as to how MK-8591 came to be is a fascinating tale of scientific discovery, and one, I would humbly surmise, is worthy of sharing with the group. Quite amazingly, MK-8591 was discovered by a Japanese soy sauce company, Yamasa Corporation, based in Japan's Chiba Prefecture. Interestingly, Japanese companies that develop soy sauce spend an exorbitant amount of research yen investigating chemicals that might influence taste. For some time, it has been known that nucleoside analogues can be used as flavoring enhancers in soy sauce. Well, back in 2001, Yamasa synthesized a molecule known as EFdA (4'-ethynyl, 2'-fluoro, 2'-deoxyadenosine). The chemists at the company were impressed with how closely the molecule resembled the structures of nucleoside reverse transcriptase inhibitors (NRTIs), one of the prevailing compounds used to treat HIV. Further testing by a famous Japanese scientist at the National Institute of Health, Hiroaki Mitsuya, who was instrumental in discovering some of the early NRTI compounds (zidovudine (AZT), didanosine (ddI), and zalcitabine (DDC)), confirmed these findings. Together with Michael Parniak, a biochemist at the University of Pittsburgh and Stefan Sarafianos, a virologist at the University of Missouri, Mitsuya spent nearly a decade uncovering the magical physical, biochemical, and biologic properties behind MK-8591. In 2012, Merck licensed in the EfDA compound from Yamasa, and, over the last five years, the team has moved EFdA (now MK-8591) through its various stages of preclinical and clinical testing. Our team is now in the late stages of Phase 2, assessing the combination of MK-8591 and doravirine (our NNRTI) as a once-daily regimen, and the early indications from this trial are extremely promising. So, we are on the cusp of a novel, profound advance for the field of HIV. How stunning! So, next time you are sipping sake and scarfing down some scrumptious sushi, please raise a glass to the stupendous serendipity of those sage soy sauce synthesizers!

Now, I don't want to leave you thinking that serendipity is a rare occurrence.

In fact, MK-8591 is just one of the many stories about happy accidents that have led to our company's success. Did you know that the natural compound avermectin that led to the development of ivermectin (MECTIZAN®) by Merck's recent Nobel laurate, Dr. William Campbell, was discovered from a soil sample collected from the Kawana Golf Course near Tokyo? Raise your sake cup again!

Then, there's another one of my favorite mistakes, caspofungin. Caspofungin is our highly successful echinocandin agent which was discovered to have antifungal properties in the mid-1980s, at a time our MRL Discovery group was seeking to develop agents to treat *Pneumocystis* pneumonia (PCP), a common complication tied to the then-burgeoning acquired immunodeficiency syndrome (AIDS) epidemic. In addition to having coverage for *P. jiroverci* (the etiologic agent that causes PCP), Merck scientists unexpectedly discovered that caspofungin's precursor, pneumocandin B_0, was also a highly effective agent against fungi, including yeast (*Candida spp.*) and mould (*Aspergillus spp.*). Well, thanks to indinavir, another Merck discovery, the number of PCP cases fell dramatically in the second half of the 1990s. So, it was only fitting that caspofungin would be repurposed to treat invasive fungal infections. Like ivermectin, pneumocandin B_0 was a natural product discovered at CIBE, a Merck Spanish subsidiary, in a non-pathogenic fungus collected from a river valley in Spain.

Outside of our own therapeutic areas, I could also point to atrepitant, a substance P antagonist. Many years back, Merck Research Laboratories (MRL) learned, after extensive evaluation, that atrepitant was not effective in treating major depressive disorder; however, chemists were fascinated to learn that the compound, with its central morpholine core, was highly-effective in curbing chemotherapy-induced nausea and vomiting (CINV). Atrepitant has now become a standard of care for CINV.

Finally, I can also point to the crown jewel in our current oncology portfolio, pembrolizumab. At the time Merck acquired Schering Plough (SP), pembrolizumab was one of the forgotten compounds acquired from SP's merger with Organon. It was not really on many folks' radar screen as a potentially powerful cancer agent, and it was mainly focused as an agent to impact immune disorders. It was only after Bristol-Myers Squibb reported early successful results with their own PD1 inhibitor in early 2010 that Merck rapidly advanced pembrolizumab through an array of clinical evaluations beginning in 2011; those efforts culminated in its initial approval for advanced melanoma in late 2014. Fast forward a few years to 2019, and pembrolizumab has now demonstrated a survival benefit, either alone or in combination with other agents, in over 15 clinical trials and has racked up about 20 FDA indications. Pembrolizumab is helping tens of thousands of patients who suffer from cancer.

The history of antimicrobial breakthroughs is crowded with chance findings that had a positive effect on science, the world, and human health. I figured it might be fun to pique your interest on this topic by sharing just a few historical examples of serendipitous discoveries. These three instances of unanticipated discoveries would not only advance anti-infective research but also change the world:

1. Probably the most famous example known to drug discovery experts in our field is tied to the discovery of one of the first antibacterial agents, penicillin. Dr. Alexander Fleming was a Scottish physician and surgeon who fought in World War I, where he was tasked with caring for debilitated soldiers suffering from horrible infected wounds. As there were not many effective antiseptic agents to treat these infections, he performed his fair share of amputations as a last-ditch effort to stem these infections. This harrowing experience had such a huge influence on Dr. Fleming that he dedicated the next 20 years of his career to looking for a cure that might prevent the complications of such horrible skin infections. He found himself analyzing the contents of various bacteria, including *Staphylococcus aureus* (*S. aureus*). Well, according to lore, Dr. Fleming had two interesting quirks: (1) he was a bit of an absent-minded professor; and (2) he relished his summer holiday breaks back in Scotland. Before leaving in July 1928 for a month-long vacation, he forgot to store away several petri dishes growing staphylococci, instead leaving them on a bench in a corner of his laboratory. Upon returning from his summer sojourn, he was surprised to discover that a few of the petri dishes, which he inadvertently left at room temperature, were growing mold. What was more exciting was the finding that those dishes growing mold had a "zone of inhibition" around the mold that prevented growth of the *S. aureus* colonies. He rightfully surmised that the mold, which was *Penicillium notatum*, was producing a substance that hindered the growth of the bacterium. A few other scientists, including Ernst Chain and Howard Florey, would later read about his published findings and elucidate the structure of the fungal-derived compound in 1938. They called it penicillin. However, they struggled to mass produce it using *P. notatum*. That's when the second serendipitous finding occurred.

One of their colleagues, Mary Hunt, found a cantaloupe at a local market covered in a pretty, golden mold. So, she bought it and brought it to their lab in Peoria, Illinois. They discovered that the mould was *P. chrysogenum*, and it yielded 200 times the amount of penicillin that Fleming's mold produced. The age of antibiotic research was founded. A decade later, Merck and three other pharmaceutical companies collaborated to mass-synthesize the antibiotic for use during World War II. For their efforts, Fleming, Chain, and Florey would be awarded the Nobel Prize in Physiology or Medicine in 1945. I'll speak more to Merck's involvement in this endeavor in a future *Thankful Thursday* segment.

2. Dr. Fleming's accidental discovery of a magic bullet to treat bacterial infections may never had taken place without the accidental discovery of how to selectively culture bacteria on a solid medium, a finding attributed to Dr. Robert Koch. Dr. Koch was a German microbiologist and physician who is eminently regarded as the Father of Modern Microbiology. His work in discovering the causative agents responsible for cholera, anthrax, and tuberculosis is pivotal to the field. Moreover, his four principles that comprise the Koch Postulates provide a foundation upon which infectious disease discovery has been based over the last 150 years. However, none of these advances would have been realized without his revolutionary method of selectively culturing bacteria on a solid medium. Up until that point, bacteria had been grown in liquid broth, so it was technically not feasible to isolate bacteria. One day, according to legend, Dr. Koch inadvertently left his unfinished lunch in his laboratory. After a long weekend, he returned to discover that part of his uneaten potato was covered by different colored growths. Those growths turned out to be colonies of bacteria. This serendipitous discovery gave Dr. Koch the idea of plating bacteria on a solid medium, as opposed to a liquid broth. He confided his finding to one of his colleagues, Julius Petri, who helped invent in a shallow jar that could be used to hold the medium. Together, Koch and Petri would invent the Petri dish as a novel vehicle to isolate, analyze, and identify bacteria. Koch's work in pure culture microbiology led to the discovery of *Mycobacterium tuberculosis* as the cause of tuberculosis, which would win him the Nobel Prize in Physiology or Medicine in 1905.
3. However, Koch would have probably never discovered the solid media phenomenon if not for the earlier work of Dr. Edward

Jenner. Dr. Jenner was integral in inspiring Koch, Pasteur, and other luminaries of the nineteenth century to prove and reconfirm the Germ theory principle. Dr. Jenner was a late eighteenth century country doctor practicing in the southwest area of Great Britain. He often cared for the farm workers who worked in the surrounding parishes. In his daily dealings, Dr. Jenner would often come across farm hands, such as milkmaids, who had sores on their hands. These sores were caused by infection from cowpox, a virus they would acquire while milking the cows. Luckily, cowpox is often a self-limiting, non-virulent disease associated with superficial skin infections. Dr. Jenner and other physicians realized that these milkmaids were some of the few parishioners in the region who would never develop smallpox. As one maid boasted to Jenner: "I shall never have smallpox for I have had cowpox. Hence, I shall never have an ugly pockmarked face." This phenomenon was interesting because smallpox was normally a highly virulent disease prevalent in the majority of those living in late eighteenth century England, routinely leading to the death of 10 to 20 percent of the entire English population. At the time, the only way to prevent smallpox was to expose an uninfected person to variolous material collected from a smallpox victim in an effort to elicit a less-severe form of the infection; however, this transfer under the skin often resulted in a life-threatening infection. Jenner postulated that the pus in the blisters that milkmaids received from cowpox could possibly protect others from smallpox. To test this hypothesis, Jenner attempted something revolutionary. In May 1796, he inoculated an 8-year-old boy named James Phipps, the son of Jenner's gardener, with cowpox in an effort to prevent the child from developing smallpox. Jenner scraped pus from cowpox blisters on the hands of a milkmaid, Sarah Nelmes; then, Jenner immediately inoculated little James in both arms. James developed a fever and became slightly queasy, but he did not develop a full-blown infection. Later, he injected Phipps with smallpox, but no disease followed. The boy was later re-challenged with a higher dose of smallpox and again showed no sign of infection. Jenner had successfully performed the first vaccine clinical trial, so named because *vacca* is the Latin word for cow. Vaccinology was discovered that day, thanks to the observations of a few milkmaids and an astute Gloucestershire physician.

Fortunately, serendipity still happens today in infectious disease research. I won't bore you with all the gory details as to how Drs. Robin Warren and Barry Marshall, two Australian scientists working in Perth, determined that *Helicobacter pylori* was the culprit responsible for acute gastritis and peptic ulcer disease. Instead, I'm attaching the link to a short, entertaining article published in *Lancet* in 2001 that recounts the story about *H. pylori*: https://www.thelancet.com/journals/lancet/article/PIIS0140-6736(05)71459-8/fulltext.

So, today, I'm thankful for those coincidental discoveries that have fortuitously changed the course of modern history and infectious disease research. Of course, I would be remiss if I pretended that all these accidental discoveries were the result of dumb luck. In fact, in a great book on the topic, *Happy Accidents: Serendipity in Modern Medical Breakthroughs*, author Morton Myers details some of the discoveries I've listed above and many more. However, in his book's introduction, Myers emphasizes that serendipity in discovery is not simply a matter of chance. Rather, advances are made only if the accidents are appreciated by those who are willing to see it. Any investigator confronted by an unintentional observation must still recognize the importance of that singular occurrence of chance and act upon it to prove its scientific validity. As Louis Pasteur once proclaimed, "chance favors only the prepared mind." Myers further acknowledges that any serendipitous findings, once fully explained, then need to serve as building blocks to inform medical research going forward. He states that medical comprehension of an unanticipated event can still inform serendipitous findings in the future, provided we maintain a willingness and openness to consider novel, if not outlandish, ideas. As we undertake our daily roles, we should be reminded that new drug discoveries will not always follow a predetermined research path, and it is perfectly acceptable to consider innovative, unprecedented ideas.

This all brings me back to MK-8591, which is quickly becoming one of my favorite mistakes. Let me take a moment to thank all those chemists in that Japanese soy sauce company for their dedicated efforts to synthesize new chemical entities that might advance the savory field of flavoring. Let me also express my fervent gratitude to all those here at Merck on our HIV early development teams, MK-8591 development teams, and their subteams, who took what Yamasa discovered and are now diligently advancing it as a new agent in the HIV armamentarium. My sincere hope is that the adventitious findings that Yamasa made leading up to the discovery of MK-8591 will be furthered by our own advancements in development. If all things progress as we've planned, MK-8591 has the potential to be a game changer, significantly impacting people living with HIV and those individuals at risk of developing HIV infection.

Now, tell me, doesn't that leave a good taste in your mouth?

14 Justice and Jubilation for Jersey *(March 28, 2019)*

For this week's *Thankful Thursday* segment, I aim to extol a place that rarely, if ever, gets the admiration, appreciation, and acknowledgement it rightfully deserves. Instead of being lauded as our nation's center of innovation, creativity, and scientific discovery, the place where I was born is routinely chastised as irrelevant, overly urbanized, and even unsightly. Well, the disrespect ends today. In today's segment, I'll dare to demonstrate why New Jersey is so deserving of our devotion. Guys and gals, I gladly give gratitude to the great Garden State!

> *"Oh, come take my hand, cause I'm riding out tonight to case the promised land."* [15]

Yes, let's follow Bruce Springsteen's advice: Please come take my hand because the season of spring is upon us. I hear the birds chirping in the morning, and I gaze upon the colorful crocuses and daffodils as they grow in my neighborhood. Such signs lend proof that indeed the season of rebirth is upon us. However, the real proof of its arrival is that the Major League Baseball season has officially commenced. Today, March 28, the Philadelphia Phillies are scheduled to play their home opener against the Atlanta Braves, as both teams vie to be one of 29 teams who might dethrone the Boston Red Sox from their champion perch. My beloved Phillies acquired much new talent in the offseason, and expectations for a successful season spring eternal. Baseball is such a wonderful, civilized game despite all of its

15 From the song "Thunder Road" by Bruce Springsteen, first recorded on the album *Born to Run* (1975).

silly quirks—like the infield fly rule, the ground-rule double, and the balk. Where else can you succeed only one third of the time and still be regarded as excellent in your trade? In what other sport do you see the manager adorning the same uniform as the players? Where else is stealing regarded as a good thing? But, despite its apparent shortcomings, it is exactly as James Earl Jones said in the movie *Field of Dreams*: "The one constant through all the years has been baseball. This field, this game, it is part of our past. It reminds us of all that once was good and could be again."

So, when we ponder about baseball and the past, it is only fitting to go to where it first was started, to the lovely town of Hoboken, New Jersey. Most folks know Hoboken as the birthplace of Frank Sinatra or a convenient place to catch a water ferry over to midtown Manhattan. However, the greatest thing that this little town on the Palisades of New Jersey has given the world has been baseball. Back in 1846, the first competitive baseball game was played at Elysian Fields between the New York Nine and the Knickerbockers. Unfortunately, it was neither a competitive nor an entertaining game (the final score was 23 to 1). Yet, a legacy was born that day.

I was also born less than two miles from Elysian Fields in Jersey City, New Jersey, and lived my first ten years entirely on the Palisades—first in the town of Fort Lee and then in Cliffside Park. In fact, the thin, 10-mile long stretch along the New Jersey Palisades between the George Washington Bridge in Fort Lee and the Holland Tunnel in Jersey City is famous for many historical events. It is here, in Weehawken, that Aaron Burr and Alexander Hamilton conducted their famous duel in 1804. A decade ago, Captain Sully decided it was a fine place to land a malfunctioning US Airways Airbus 320. And who could forget Bridgegate, the subtle, tactful decision by Governor Christie administration (please note the Jersey sarcasm) to punish the Fort Lee mayor with the prolonged closure of a few lanes as part of a so-called traffic study?

Besides baseball, New Jersey is famous for many firsts in sports. On the athletic front, the first college football game was played in New Brunswick, New Jersey, in 1869. In fact, that event celebrates its 150th anniversary later this year. When that game was over, the Rutgers Queensmen had defeated the College of New Jersey (now Princeton) Tigers in a hard-fought battle, winning 6 to 4. How is that score even possible? The first professional basketball game was also played in

New Jersey in 1896. The Trenton, New Jersey, team defeated the Brooklyn Club, 16 to 1. Again, how is that score even possible? But, I'm not here to discuss sports, though I could wax poetic on this topic for an excruciatingly long time. I'm here today to show you why we owe New Jersey so much when it comes to our daily existences.

> *"I spent 20 years trying to get out of this place. I was looking for something I couldn't replace. I was running away from the only thing I've ever known."*[16]

These Bon Jovi lyrics tell my own story, but I truly believe the world owes so much to this small, peninsular state nestled between New York City and Philadelphia. In my estimation, New Jersey is the forgotten state, partly due to its small size (fourth smallest in the US) and partly because many of us only experience this great state in bumper-to-bumper traffic while traveling on the New Jersey Turnpike. Yet, I would argue that everyone has some connection to the state in one way or another:

- **Your connection may be historical**: Many of our ancestors entered this country through Ellis Island, that small island off the coast of New Jersey. Not too long ago, the first glimpse immigrants would get of New Jersey was of the lovely Statue of Liberty, which has resided on the Jersey side in the Hudson harbor since 1875. Unfortunately, today it seems the first glimpse folks get upon arriving in New Jersey are of Linden's oil refineries, as planes land at Liberty Newark Airport, one of our nation's busiest airport.
- **Your connection may even be cultural**: What New Jersey has bestowed on us culturally is simply amazing. New Jersey is the home of some of the greatest musicians of all time. I've already alluded to Frank Sinatra, but were you aware that the nation's third state to ratify the Constitution is also the birthplace of William "Count" Basie, Paul Simon, Frankie Vallie, Clint Black, and Dionne Warwick? What kind of person would I be if I did not call out some of my favorite New Jersey musical legends, such as Les Paul, Bon Jovi, and, the Boss (Bruce Springsteen)? When it comes to artists, we can thank New Jersey for everything from the *Red Badge of Courage* by Stephen Crane, to the Beat Generation's Allen Ginsburg, and even to *The Game of Thrones* by George R.R.

---

16 From the song "You Says You Can't Go Home" by Bon Jovi, first recorded on the album *Have a Nice Day* (2006).

Martin. Without the Garden State, there would be no Abbott and Costello, no Jason Alexander playing George Costanza, no Christopher Reeve playing Superman, and no Tom Cruise in *Top Gun*.

- **Your connection may also be practical:** The conveniences that New Jerseyans have imparted to us are too numerous to count. Several of our common, everyday amenities have come from this great state, including air conditioning, the transistor, and liquid crystal display (LCD); by the way, we couldn't power our high-definition televisions without the latter two items. We can partake of M&M'S, ice cream cones, condensed soup, and saltwater taffy—all because of this great state. Heck, it even introduced us to the quintessential roadside diner, where you can get anything on the menu from pasta to souvlaki. New Jersey boasts the most diners in the world, about 525 in total, and most of them are open 24 hours a day. When was the last time anyone left a good New Jersey diner unsatisfied with their meal or complaining that the portion was too small? It just doesn't happen.
- **Finally, your connection may simply be inspirational**: Let's take a moment to consider what New Jerseyans have invented throughout history. Besides electricity, which I'll come back to in a second, many other greatest inventions were created in the Garden State. Perhaps the reason why New Jerseyans are so resilient is that everything that protects us, whether its Band-Aids or Teflon or even Bubble Wrap, had its bold beginning here. Even those annoying anti-theft tags they put on clothing merchandise in retail shops originated in New Jersey. Thanks to its ingenious native Les Paul, we now can rock to the solid-body electric guitar that bears his name (Gibson Les Paul) or blissfully enjoy music recorded on a multi-track platform. In fact, multi-track recording was first used on the Beatles' *St. Pepper's Lonely Hearts Club Band*, my favorite album of all time! For all these reasons, you should not be surprised to learn that New Jersey is the only state in the country with its own Inventors Hall of Fame. But, this is just the beginning.

"I faced it all and I stood tall, and I did it my way."[17]

17 From the song "My Way" by Paul Anka (1967). The song was made popular by Frank Sinatra in 1969.

When one thinks about scientific discovery, medical innovation, and the importance of the pharmaceutical industry, the conversation cannot start without acknowledging the great state nestled between the Hudson and Delaware rivers. Here's a statistic you probably did not know: New Jersey has more scientists per square mile than any other place in the world. If it weren't for those New Jerseyans who dared to experiment scientifically, that is, doing it in their own way, as Frank Sinatra says in the lyrics above, the world would not be the same.

When it comes to New Jersey's role in scientific discovery and invention, we need to harken back to the second half of the nineteenth century. At that time, in the face of the Industrial Revolution, the state of New Jersey transformed itself from an agrarian society into an industry-focused powerhouse. Companies sought to establish factories in the sprawling space the Garden State could afford while still maintaining a convenient proximity to large cities, such as New York and Philadelphia. Cities like Paterson, Trenton, and Newark emerged as hubs of textile and silk production. Inventions like the steam locomotive and steam boat, both of which were conceived in New Jersey, helped facilitate the exportation of finished commodities outside of the state. And, at around that same time, a poor Ohio boy named Thomas Alva Edison moved to New Jersey and started to get busy. He invented the light bulb, the incandescent lamp, the phonograph, motion pictures, fluoroscopy, and the carbon telephone transmitter. In fact, it took fewer than four years between the time Edison invented the light bulb, in 1879, and the time the first incandescent lighting system, which used electricity via an overheard wiring system, was installed in Roselle, NJ, in 1883. As the Wizard of Menlo Park, Edison created the first industrial research laboratories, from which he would file and receive 1,093 patents during his lifetime. Taken together, the Industrial Revolution and the arrival of Thomas Edison set up New Jersey nicely for future innovation.

At around that time, our knowledge of medicine also started to flourish. In the nineteenth century, small apothecaries began producing remedies to treat common medical ailments. A large number of these chemistry-focused companies had their roots in Germany. As many of these German chemists migrated to the New World during the late 1800s, an industry started to take hold in the mid-Atlantic region. Take, for instance, Pfizer Inc., which was initially founded in 1849 in New York City by two German immigrants,

Charles Pfizer and Charles Erhart, to produce fine chemicals[18]. It then transitioned to develop pharmaceutical products, such as painkillers and antiseptic compounds, in the 1860s during the Civil War. Similarly, a physician in the US Navy named Edward Robinson Squibb who served in the US-Mexican War (1846-1848) became famous in 1854 for devising a simple method of ether distillation. During the Civil War, Squibb set up his own pharmaceutical business in Brooklyn, ultimately providing our troops morphine and other surgical anesthetics, as well as quinine to treat malaria. One of the colonels in the Union cavalry, Eli Lilly, was so intrigued by these medicinal products that he set up his own pharmaceutical business after the war. Finally, another visionary, Robert Wood Johnson, who had built a sterile goods company in New Brunswick, NJ, chose to expand into the medicinal chemistry area when he saw the success of others, such as Pfizer and Squibb.

It's against this backdrop that Merck also came to reside in New Jersey. In the late nineteenth century, a German pharmaceutical company, which was founded in 1648 by the Merck family in the town of Darmstadt and had popularized the commercial manufacture of morphine in Germany, decided to seize on the opportunity to establish a subsidiary in New York. So, they sent a family member, George F. Merck, across the Atlantic in 1891, and he proceeded to set up shop in New York City, following in the footsteps of Pfizer and Squibb. Although George operated the US subsidiary for Merck out of Manhattan for about a decade, even opening a pharmacy in Manhattan in 1897, he quickly realized the need to have more physical space to expand his chemical manufacturing business. Hence, in 1900, he purchased 150 acres across the Hudson River in Rahway, New Jersey. Three years later, George would settle in Rahway with 20 employees, two buildings, and two working telephones. Over time, his oldest son and company heir, George W. Merck, realized that he needed to expand on what Edison was doing in places like Menlo Park and West Orange and develop a pharmaceutical research center in Rahway (**Figure 8**). So, in 1933, George W. established Merck's Research and Development division—a novel concept at the time. Following Edison's example, George W. set up a university-like setting to help attract research talent from local academic powerhouses, such as Princeton University, Rutgers University, the NJ Institute of Technology, and Stevens

18 Fine chemicals are pure chemical substances produced in limited quantities according to exacting specifications.

Institute of Technology. Like Merck, many of the other pharmaceutical companies at that time would settle in New Jersey, including Johnson & Johnson, Squibb, and Schering Corporation. New Jersey was now the preeminent center for pharmaceutical research (**Figure 9**).

These fortuitous events would lead to more than a century of biomedical innovation and pharmaceutical discovery in the state of New Jersey. The discovery that was probably most relevant to the Merck Infectious Disease group was streptomycin, which was first discovered by a PhD student, Albert Schatz, in the laboratory of Dr. Selman Waksman at Rutgers University. Streptomycin, the first antibiotic to target tuberculosis, was borne out of a collaborative research program funded by Merck. Its discovery led to Merck's introduction of this antibiotic to the market several years later. In a bit of controversy, Schatz's involvement in the discovery would be underplayed, as Waksman became the sole recipient of the Nobel Prize of Physiology or Medicine in 1952. We'll talk about streptomycin a bit more in a future *Thankful Thursday* segment, but, for now, let's just say that its availability helped to revolutionize the treatment of tuberculosis and put an end to quarantining tuberculosis-infected patients in sanitariums. In addition to streptomycin, Merck would proceed to synthesize the Vitamin B complex and many other vitamins, penicillin, and cortisone in its research facilities in Rahway, NJ (**Figure 10**). A few years later, a group of scientists at the Schering Corporation would synthesize prednisone at their facility in Bloomfield, NJ. And the hits would keep on coming for pharmaceutical discoveries in New Jersey. In due time, the state would be the founding place for other antibiotics such as tetracycline, which was developed by scientists at Lederle. Key discoveries in treatments for non-infectious diseases, including the oral angiotensin-converting enzyme inhibitor captopril, which was developed by Bristol-Myers Squibb, and benzodiazepine diazepam, which was developed by Hoffman-La Roche, had their birthplace in the Garden State as well.

Altogether, the scientific world and medical innovation owe much to the achievements that have come from the great Garden State. Yet, New Jersey never seems to get the appreciation it fully deserves. Instead of singing about New Jersey, Hoboken's own Frank Sinatra opted instead to serenade another city in his song "New York, New York." The pundits on late night television are constantly using the state or its nine million inhabitants as a punchline in their opening monologues. The Jersey accent and the wild hair styles on the Jersey shore make an easy target for any comedian, and the lack of scenery along the New Jersey Turnpike and the unbearable traffic, especially in Fort Lee, are fodder for talk show jokes. Even professional sports teams that physically play in New Jersey, like the Giants and Jets, still claim New York as their base. In fact, the only professional sports team that claims New Jersey in its name happens to be called the Devils. Really? That's just not right. I also find it annoying when visitors to the United States claim they flew into New York, but only later do I discover that they really landed at Liberty Newark Airport.

I must admit I also have my own issues with a few of New Jersey's quirks and peccadillos. Like, why must I go to the right, into a jug handle, to make a left-hand turn? And, why can't I pump my own gasoline on a New Jersey Parkway service plaza? And why would anyone care what "Snooki" and "The Situation" are doing at the Jersey Shore this weekend? Due to these and other oddities, everyone tends to make fun of New Jersey.

I think I've finally realized why.

It happens because everyone else who is not from New Jersey is just plain jealous. Just like New Jersey's native son Jack Nicholson once said, the world simply "can't handle the truth" that New Jerseyans have changed the world. It is a hard pill to swallow, but no one can deny that the world would not be where it is today without all that New Jersey has provided us. Modern sports wouldn't be where they stand today without the firsts that happened in New Jersey. We would be lacking in the conveniences of our modern lives without the advancements in art, technology, and cuisine that New Jersey has afforded us. Without New Jersey's scientific advancements in medicinal chemistry, I surmise that Merck and most other pharmaceutical companies wouldn't be where they currently are. Thus, today, I'm thankful to the great Garden State of New Jersey. I'm also grateful for all my colleagues in our New Jersey facilities, including Rahway and Kenilworth, for all they've done and continue to do to support Merck. I am grateful for all you have given me, my company, and the world.

Although they've taken the home away from this boy, no one can take this boy away from his true home. The streets along the Palisades are my streets, and I'm proud to call myself a native New Jerseyan. In fact, I'm a better person because of it.

So, next time, you see someone making fun of New Jersey, tell them what Jon Bon Jovi says:

"When the world keeps trying to drag me down,
I've gotta raise my hands, gonna stand my ground.
Cause when the world gets in my face,
Well, I say, 'Have a nice day.'"

15 A Timely Tribute to the True Titans of Our Trials (April 11, 2019)

For this week's *Thankful Thursday* segment, I'd like to express my wholehearted appreciation to all individuals who consent to participate in our clinical trials. The advancement of medical knowledge is contingent on the support and kindness of our study participants. Hence, it is only fitting that I take a moment to acknowledge their selfless sacrifice for the sake of science.

In the past, I've shared several anecdotes as to how medical knowledge has progressed as a result of clinical experiments. In the segment on serendipity, I recounted the story of James Phipps, the 8-year-old neighbor of Dr. Edward Jenner, who became the first person to be vaccinated with the cowpox virus. In turn, Phipps developed immunity against smallpox, a finding confirmed when Phipps did not succumb to smallpox even after experimental exposures to variolous material. I could also relay the story of Sir Joseph Lister and his experimental use of carbolic acid as an antiseptic to prevent wound infections following orthopedic surgery. As the "Father of Modern Surgery," Lister ushered in a new era of infection control. These two accounts, which chronicle a few of the first clinical experiments, were instrumental in furthering our comprehension of vaccinology and preventive care.

I chose the timing for this segment to coincide with a famous medical announcement that occurred 64 years ago. On April 12, 1955, a diminutive spectacled physician from the University of Pittsburgh approached a podium in Ann Arbor, Michigan, and publicly announced the results of the largest clinical trial to have been conducted in the history of humankind. As a virologist and medical researcher, Jonas Salk had developed a polio vaccine using three inactivated strains of poliovirus. His vaccine was extensively evaluated in a clinical trial that would change the course of medical research forever. However, to truly appreciate the sheer magnitude of this achievement, one really needs to fully understand how the first successful polio vaccine came into being. Please join me as I recount the tale of how an entire nation came together to defeat the dreaded enterovirus that causes polio. I'll also share the story of the first randomized clinical trial and how its fundamental underpinnings have helped shape the way we conduct research today. Both stories are particularly relevant to the ongoing work we do in advancing infectious disease and vaccine research here at Merck and in the pharmaceutical industry as a whole.

The Rally Cry Against Polio

In 1921, a practicing lawyer in New York named Franklin Delano Roosevelt was vacationing on an island off the state of Maine when he came down with a febrile illness characterized by a facial palsy, bladder and bowel dysfunction, and ascending paralysis. Although many of the symptoms resolved, Roosevelt would remain permanently paralyzed from the waist down. Roosevelt was diagnosed with paralytic polio, though, in retrospect, he might have suffered from Guillain-Barre syndrome. Despite his disability, Roosevelt remained an active civil servant in the Empire State, ultimately making his way to the Governor's Mansion in Albany, New York, in 1929, and then to the White House as the elected President of the United States in 1932.

Roosevelt was viewed by many as an incredible stalwart who not only persevered but even flourished despite his disability. Although he ascended to the presidency in the tumultuous time of the Great Depression, Roosevelt was prolific in setting a clear vision and strong path to restore a struggling nation. As television was not existent at that time, he used as series of radio fireside chats to communicate with the populace in a bold, self-assured way about programs that would restore the American economy. His New Deal program, Works Relief Program, and Social Security Board would help to revive our nation. By the end of Roosevelt's presidency, the US economy was improving. His tenacious, can-do attitude and steadfast optimism inspired a recovering nation to believe that anything was possible with a bullish recipe of foresight, diligence, and stamina.

In this setting, Roosevelt decided to appeal to the American public to address an epidemic that was taking hold in the United States. In an environment of poverty caused by to the Great Depression, polio has spread widely throughout the United States, crippling 10,000 to 60,000 children each summer. So, on January 3, 1938, Roosevelt asked Americans to contribute whatever they could to the National Foundation of Infantile Paralysis (NFIP), a foundation he created with his legal colleague, Basil O'Connor, to tackle polio. At one of the early fundraising events, the celebrity singer Eddie Cantor joked that Americans should send whatever spare change they could muster to the White House for research against polio, even referring to it as a *March of Dimes* (a play of words on a popular radio show at that time, the *March of Time*). Well, the American public responded to the challenge, and millions of dimes and dollars poured into the White House. In fact, one estimate states that about 2.7 million dimes were sent to the White House that winter. Similar fundraisers would occur over the next decade to support the effort.

The research that sprang from the *March of Dimes* initiative changed the world's understanding of polio. As a direct result of this philanthropic funding, researchers unearthed the three different poliovirus serotypes that cause the paralytic disease, and they even developed techniques to cultivate the polio virus in culture. Early research funding also helped ascertain that the virus needed to enter the bloodstream to cause the paralytic disease, but antisera from polio victims could help curb the neurological complications. Most importantly, the funding also supported research into vaccine development. Now, it is important to realize that a few vaccines to prevent polio had been developed by 1935, but the efficacy data on these vaccines was unconvincing, as no formal clinical trials had been performed. When a few deaths were seen following vaccination with one of the early vaccines, the early vaccines were quickly discarded. However, the NFIP remained steadfast in its pursuit of a preventive tool against polio. The foundation funded research by a young, aspiring virologist named Dr. Jonas Salk to develop an inactivated vaccine against the three polio strains.

Jonas Salk formulated the first effective polio vaccine in 1952. His vaccine included three wild-type, virulent reference strains of polio (Types 1, 2, and 3 polio) harvested in Vero cells. Once cultivated in culture, the viruses were then inactivated with formalin. When the vaccine was injected under the skin, it would elicit neutralizing antibodies in the bloodstream, protecting an individual from the complications of the enterovirus infection. Even if a vaccinated person contracted polio in his intestine, that infection would fail to progress into frank viremia, a requisite step before the virus could settle in motor neurons. By early 1953, Salk had tested his vaccine prototype on 26 children and adults with success. However, for the world to truly accept the effectiveness and tolerability of a vaccine, a large clinical trial would need to be performed.

But before I discuss the design and results of the Francis Field Trial—the large 1954 study that would confirm the efficacy and safety of the Salk polio vaccine—we need to take a slight digression and learn about the first randomized clinical trial, which was conducted nearly a decade earlier in the United Kingdom.

The Scientific Significance of the Streptomycin Study

In a recent *Thankful Thursday* segment, I highlighted the work of Rutgers biologists Albert Schatz and Selman Waksman, who discovered streptomycin in a soil-based fungus. While digging in the dirt in 1943, Schatz uncovered a compound that effectively curtailed the growth of *Mycobacterium tuberculosis*, the bacteria responsible for tuberculosis, both *in vitro* and *in vivo* in a guinea pig model. Schatz and Waksman are proof that, irrespective of what your parents once warned, playful waddling in the mud can reap massive rewards.

A few preliminary, anecdotal reports in infected patients had suggested that streptomycin was a promising candidate against tuberculosis. The FDA approved streptomycin in 1945 without any clinical trials (a requirement that would not come into being until the enactment of Kefauver-Harris Amendment to the Federal Food, Drug, and Cosmetic Act in 1962). So in 1946, Merck started to mass produce streptomycin from a manufacturing plant in Elkton, Virginia.

In the financially-constrained, post-war era, the United Kingdom had purchased about 50 kg of streptomycin for testing in patients with tuberculosis to see if this was worthy of further investment. The decision as to how to best use the streptomycin was left to the Medical Research Council (MRC), which was a UK advisory council responsible for medical fund distribution. The MRC was a well-respected entity that had transformed medicine in the early twentieth century. The council helped fund critical research that led to the identification of the virus responsible for the influenza epidemic. The MRC also assisted in the experimental fermentation of penicillin.

The MRC established a committee to design a trial to evaluate streptomycin. After much deliberation, the committee opted to perform a trial using a 1:1 randomization scheme. About 100 young adults 30 to 50 years of age with acute progressive bilateral pulmonary tuberculosis were enrolled. At the time, the standard of care for tuberculosis was bed rest, often in sanitariums with other infected patients. Several clinical researchers, including Drs. Marc Daniels, D'Arcy Hart, and Bradford Hill, designed a trial to compare streptomycin and best rest vs. bed rest alone.

What they did in this specific trial was something that had not been done before and that helped transform clinical research going forward. Previously, the standard of clinical research was to alternately allocate subjects to the experimental group or the control group. Now, however, they allocated participants using envelopes containing randomly assigned numbers. Subjects received whatever treatment was indicated in the next envelope. Hence, the streptomycin trial became the first prospective, multicenter, *randomized* trial.

The results of this study were instrumental in confirming the efficacy of streptomycin. After 6 months, the overall mortality was 7 percent (4/55) in the streptomycin group vs. 29 percent (15/52) in the control group. After 12 months, the mortality was 22 percent in the streptomycin group vs. 46 percent in the control group. The higher mortality in months 7 to 12 as compared to months 1 to 6 in the active streptomycin group was the direct result of streptomycin resistance, a new phenomenon not fully understood at that time. Hence, this small trial of about 100 subjects not only confirmed the value of streptomycin, but also confirmed the benefit would likely be short-lived unless streptomycin resistance could be curtailed. Fortunately, two other, novel agents, para-aminosalicylic acid and isoniazid, would soon be discovered and used in combination with streptomycin to effectively treat tuberculosis.

The Fulfillment of the Francis Field Trial

Against this backdrop, the head of the NFIP, Basil O'Connor, began preparing a trial to evaluate the Salk vaccine. He asked a University of Michigan virologist, Thomas Francis, who had been the first person to isolate influenza in the US and was an active leader of influenza vaccine research, to design and lead the Salk vaccine trial. Francis had mentored Salk on vaccine methodology when Salk visited the University of Michigan in the 1940s, so the two scientists knew and respected each other.

Many endless debates would take place as to how to best evaluate the Salk vaccine. On the one hand, there were the purists who really wanted to conduct a randomized, placebo-control trial, commensurate to that done a few years earlier by the MRC, to confirm streptomycin's effectiveness. The proponents strongly held that such a design was critical to cast away any uncertainties that might be raised by vaccine doubters, especially following the failures of the earlier (1935) polio vaccines. On the other hand, there were the pragmatists who felt an observed-control trial was needed to garner support for the vaccine and minimize the number of subjects exposed to placebo. In the end, a decision was made to include both components into a single trial, which would turn out to be the largest and most expensive scientific experiment performed to date. Over 1.8 million second and third grade children would be enrolled in the year-long trial, with 400 thousand enrolled in the placebo-controlled component (200 thousand receiving the Salk vaccine and 200 thousand receiving an indistinguishably-matched saline injection), and 1.08 million enrolled in the observed-control component (220 thousand receiving vaccine and the remainder serving as observed controls). The study staff involved over 100 individuals from the University of Michigan School of Public Health, and the trial cost an unprecedented $5 million in direct costs. Children from the US, Canada, and Finland participated in the trial.

One can only imagine the buzz and excitement in the Rackham Auditorium at the University of Michigan as Drs. Francis and Salk approached the podium and shared the results on April 12, 1955. The vaccine was indeed effective in preventing paralytic polio (about 78 percent efficacy in the randomized component and 90 percent in the observed component). Specifically, the efficacy against serotypes

1, 2, and 3 was estimated at 60-70 percent, about 95 percent, and about 95 percent, respectively. More importantly, the vaccine was well tolerated. The words that Francis used to start his speech to the packed-filled auditorium say it all: "The vaccine works. It is safe, effective, and potent." Applause broke out in the auditorium as Salk approached the stage and shared his perspective. I can only imagine how proud Roosevelt might have felt were he present in Ann Arbor to see his idea for the NFIP come to fruition. Sadly, Roosevelt would not live to see that day, as he died of polio while in office at the age of 63 on April 12, 1945, exactly ten years before the Salk vaccine announcement.

Our country has chosen to commemorate the vision behind the *March of Dimes* campaign by engraving Roosevelt's bust on the US dime. However, no one has taken a moment to thank those 1.8 million who graciously participated in the Francis Field Trial. It is only fitting that we pause to praise all those children (and their parents) who consented to participate in that experiment. Many of those surviving individuals are now in their seventh decade of life, and, in fact, might be loved ones you know. Due to their steadfast courage and enthusiastic willingness to join in the most important clinical experiment ever conducted, a vaccine to treat polio would quickly become a fixture in the preventive care of all children. The Salk vaccine, which is still used in the US today, successfully reduced the number of polio cases from 35,000 in 1953 to 5,600 by 1957. By 1961, the number of polio cases in the US was down to 161, and, by 1979, the US had successfully eradicated polio. Polio was effectively eliminated from all the Americas by 1994, and we now stand on the brink of global polio elimination, with only 33 global cases reported worldwide in 2018 (**Figure 11**).

I should also thank those patients who participated in the streptomycin trial. At the time that UK study was performed by the MRC, informed consent was not a standard approach. In fact, the adults who participated in that trial were not even aware of their participation until after the 15-month study period had ended—an idea that would seem frighteningly foreign to us today. So, all those Brits who were involved in the streptomycin trial are particularly worthy of our appreciation—if not apology—for being subjugated to a treatment they had not consented to.

Today, hundreds of thousands of patients voluntarily participate in global clinical trial research. The latest report on Global Clinical Trial Participation, which was released by the FDA in 2017, provides a fascinating snapshot of trial participation in those studies that supported FDA approvals of novel drug applications during 2015 and 2016. Based on the data, approximately 60,000 individuals participate in such clinical trials annually. Interestingly, even though the US makes up only 4 percent of the global population, over 30 percent who participate are US residents. Following the US, you might be surprised to find that Russia, Germany, Poland, and Czech Republic are the top participating countries, but those five still only account for about 16 percent of the total trial participation. A recent 2017 survey conducted by the Center for Information and Study on Clinical Research Participation found that study participation remains a highly altruistic endeavor. Most of the people who participate in clinical trials do so for one of three main reasons: to help advance science (49 percent), obtain a better treatment (44 percent), or to help others with the same condition (39 percent).

Today, I am thankful for all individuals throughout the world who graciously consent to participate in our clinical trials. Without their resolve, altruism, and courage, our advancement of clinical science and of treatment modalities would cease. Many individuals willingly participate in a clinical study without any guarantee that they will benefit from the treatment under evaluation, and each takes a calculated risk that the final trial results might show that they were assigned to a group that received a less effective treatment. How daunting is it to consider that these folks opt to enroll in an experiment, even when they fully comprehend that they might not benefit from the therapy and may even have unanticipated side effects? I extend my gratitude to all those adults and children who have the tenacity, intrepidness, and kindness to sign a trial consent.

Finally, I need to conclude with an important confession. The idea for this *Thankful Thursday* segment is not my own. Let it be known that this segment was the brainchild of my trusted colleague, Mary Beth Dorr, so please join me in thanking her for this thoughtful concept. I hope I've given the topic and the stalwart volunteers who participate in clinical research the acknowledgment they fully deserve.

16 Conferring Care for Our Cuddly Companions and Other Cardinal Creatures *(April 18, 2019)*

For this week's *Thankful Thursday* segment, I'd like to show my appreciation to our comrades who ardently advocate for the livelihood and welfare of animals. I offer praise to our deserving Merck Animal Health colleagues who are entrusted with the wellbeing of many of those furry friends and cardinal creatures that grace our homes, farms, and stables. Similarly, I offer praise to those scientists and veterinarians at other corporate, public, and academic entities striving to meet the same goal.

Before I laud our Animal Health division, I want to share a brief story with you about Jango Fett. Some of you might recall from your binge-watching escapades of *Star Wars* that Jango Fett was the preeminent bounty hunter in that galaxy far, far away. Equipped with retractable wrist blades, dual-blaster pistols, and a harnessed jet pack, Jango Fett was a formidable warrior. Unfortunately, his fool-hearted decision to ally himself with the Dark Side and the abominable Darth Tyranus would ultimately lead to his downfall in the epic Battle of Geonosis. However, his legacy would live on in his mercenary son, Boba Fett, as well as in the thousands of clones who were mass produced by the Evil Republic using Jango Fett's DNA.

Now, what you are probably less cognizant of is that Jango Fett's legacy also lives on in the Kartsonis household. Jango Fett was the name affectionately chosen for our household's adorable Golden Retriever by my three sons, who, as you might imagine, were a bit obsessed with *Star Wars*. In fact, I have chosen to commemorate Merck Animal Health (MAH) today because the Kartsonis household is officially celebrating Jango's 10th birthday this week. Born on April 17, 2009, Jango was the last remaining puppy in the April litter at the breeder's home in Princeton. The decision to purchase Jango was not one made in haste. For many years leading up to this decision, our three children, especially our middle son, Sam, advocated relentlessly for a family dog. As two working physicians, my wife, Daisy, and I tried desperately to disregard the incessant pestering of our sons. Heck, we even acquiesced to hosting a "puppy party" for Sam's seventh birthday celebration, to which we invited his ten closest friends and our friends' and neighbors' dogs to our home. In retrospect, the idea of organizing a party with dogs was a horrible idea and one any astute lawyer friend would have advised against. However, at the time, we hoped it would stave off what we failed to appreciate was an inevitability. Unfortunately, the party had the opposite effect, and Sam's insistence intensified, including pleas that he would personally care for, feed, and groom whatever Golden Retriever we chose.

As an aside, let me offer up a hard-learned life lesson to those parents with small children who are contemplating the purchase of a pet: Any child who passionately promises he/she will care for the new furry, family addition is simply not being truthful. At the end of the day, a pet automatically becomes the sole responsibility of the adults in the household. This is a proven fact. Case closed.

Nonetheless, in early June 2009, we set off on one momentous Saturday to lovely Princeton, New Jersey, where a reputable dog breeder who raised gorgeous Golden Retrievers resided. As we prepared to depart our home for this family trek, Daisy informed the boys that we were simply visiting the breeder, and they should not expect anything further. However, after we packed the kids in the back seat, Daisy asked me if I had my checkbook, and I responded: "Wait ... why do I need my checkbook, if we are only looking?" She smiled at me without saying a word, at which point I realized we would be coming home with one more child than when we left the residence. I did not object, as I secretly longed for a dog as well. At the breeder, we encountered two lovable, light yellow Golden Retriever puppies. With one already spoken for, a cuddly male retriever was the only remaining option. He would turn out to be the best option. After a quick trip to the Princeton PetSmart® to purchase some bare essentials, we headed back home with a puppy in our possession. The ride home was filled with vociferous debate over his name. Several endearing characters from *Star Wars*, including Boba Fett and Chewy, were top contenders, as was the name Chase, recognizing the Phillies had just won the World Series in the autumn of 2008. We all agreed on "Jango" for its uniqueness and euphony.

Now, Jango has been a constant force and wonderful complement to the Kartsonis family. Basically, he is my fourth son, and he is treated as such. Not only is Jango a calming presence but also a trusting, endearing companion. He offers his unconditional love to each family member and, essentially, any other human he has the distinct pleasure to encounter. Despite his large frame and a volatile weight somewhere north of 70 pounds, he lacks any truly intimidating qualities. Jango rarely barks, is incapable of harming a living soul, and has never mastered the art of growling. He'll gleefully permit you to rub his belly or pet his ears for as long as you are willing or until perpetuity, whichever comes first. His reaction to going on a walk rivals that of a 5-year old child learning his/her parents have just booked a week-long vacation to Disney World. His requisite for a daily walk has improved our physical livelihood, and his unmitigated love has enhanced our emotional wellbeing. To put it bluntly, Jango is the greatest dog that has ever lived. As a scientist, I'm sharing a photo to provide incontrovertible proof to any and all doubters (**Figure 12**).

I surmise that many of you own a similar, sweet sidekick, and I'll boldly presume that, like Jango, your pet is your consummate compadre. So it should not come as a major surprise to hear that I gladly cater to my furry friend with all the best that modern medicine has to offer. Jango is indeed the fortunate beneficiary of the vast menu of pet products offered by the MAH division. He receives *Tri-Heart Plus®*, a combination of ivermectin and pyrantel, to prevent him from falling prey to heartworms, other roundworms, and other pesky parasites such as ascarids and hookworms. Once a quarter, Jango is also rewarded a chewable, tasty treat, in the form of BRAVECTO®, which prevents him from acquiring fleas and ticks. He also has a *Home Again®* microchip, which was painlessly inserted between his shoulder blades, in the event he ever wanders off from our home. Of course, it defies logic why his royal canine majesty would ever choose to leave his lush kingdom where his grateful human servants wait on his every need; however, in the unlikely event that Jango suffers some existential crisis and chooses to brave it on his own, or perhaps more likely, he chooses to break his electrical fence and chase our wonderful, treat-bearing mailperson, it is comforting to know that King Charlemagne would soon be returned to his rightful dominion and reunited with his loyal subjects.

All kidding aside, I am amazed by the breadth and depth of animal products offered by the MAH division. In addition to *Tri-Heart®*, BRAVECTO®, and *Home Again®*, MAH offers a wide array of other products for our dogs and cats. MAH develops innovative medicines like SCALIBOR® Protector Brand, an odorless leash that gradually emits a substance that kills the ticks that may transmit Lyme disease, babesiosis, or other rickettsia diseases, such as Rocky Mountain Spotted Fever, anaplasmosis, and human ehrlichiosis. MAH creates a wide variety of vaccines that protect our canine comrades from rabies, leptospirosis, Lyme, various respiratory viruses, including canine adenovirus, coronavirus, influenza, and parainfluenza, and many more pathogens. MAH vaccines afford protections to our cats from feline leukemia, panleukopenia, and respiratory pathogens such as calcivirus and influenza. MAH even developed drugs like VETSULIN®, the only FDA-approved insulin for use in diabetic dogs and cats and SALIX®, an antidiuretic to treat edema caused by cardiac and non-cardiac conditions in dogs, cats, and horses. Speaking of horses, MAH has developed vaccines that protect our equine friends from tetanus, influenza, and viral encephalomyelitis, including West Nile virus and the Eastern, Western, and Venezuelan strains of equine encephalitis viruses.

MAH has also created a wide array of products that assist farmers in ensuring the health and wellbeing of farm animals, including sheep, cattle, swine, and poultry. Vaccines have been licensed to protect chickens, ducks, and turkeys from dreaded conditions such as *Salmonella enteritides, Bordatella avium*, coccidiosis, and avian encephalomyelitis. The research and development division within MAH have developed innovative technologies that facilitate the storage and preparation of live viral vaccines or enhance vaccine delivery systems in both small and large farm animals. The MAH team has also been instrumental in rapidly developing vaccines to address emerging epidemics. Let me share a case in point. Nearly a decade ago a certain orthobunyavirus, called Schmallenberg virus, attacked livestock in Germany, the Netherlands, Belgium, France, and other European countries, resulting in congenital malformations and stillbirths in cattle, sheep, and goats. MAH rapidly responded to the crisis by developing and licensing the first vaccine against the virus. Such veterinary vaccines not only improve the livelihood of the animals on our farms but also constitute an alternative approach to antibiotics, thereby limiting the exposure of animals on our food chain to antimicrobial agents.

One fun fact worth noting is that MAH has been developing products to support animal health for over eight decades. Back in the 1940s, one of the great problems of farming chickens and turkeys under crowded conditions was avine coccidiosis, a parasitic infection caused by the genus *Eimeria* which afflicts young chicks. Once infected, the birds grow very ill and debilitated, often with a compromised digestion. Death is common. At the time of the Great Depression and the ensuing World War conflict, it was often difficult to contain coccidiosis, and our nation's supply of poultry was routinely compromised. In fact, in the late 1940s, it was estimated that the disease cost the US poultry industry approximately $10 million—an exorbitant amount for that time. However, when sulfonamides first appeared on the market in the 1930s to treat human infections—thanks in large part to Merck and other pharmaceutical companies—researchers began to wonder whether these sulfa drugs could also control coccidiosis. Although many argued it was best to use these drugs as a treatment in infected birds, studies in the late 1940s suggested that including a sulfa drug in the feed could effectively prevent the infection. At this same time, Merck developed the sulfa agent sulfaquinoxaline. Interestingly, the drug was originally targeted for use in human malaria, but it was found to be too toxic for human use. Instead, with burgeoning research on sulfa drugs as anticoccidial agents, Merck repurposed sulfaquinoxaline and relicensed it as SQ® (for sulfaquinoxaline) for poultry coccidiosis in 1948 (**Figure 13**). This move gave birth to the MAH pharmaceutical industry. Eventually, our understanding of resistance would call into question the use of antibiotics as coccidiostats. Today, MAH offers a live vaccine, COCCIVAC®, that is administered by spray on day one of a chick's life.

Speaking of veterinary antibiotic use, it is important to acknowledge that MAH still produces various antimicrobial agents to treat and prevent infections in pets, livestock, and farm-grown, aquatic creatures, such as salmon. In fact, MAH has developed policies to ensure the responsible use of antibiotics to improve and maintain the health of domesticated animals. For a variety of reasons, society would like to get to a point where all infectious diseases in animals can be addressed through vaccination; however, several animal-borne infections remain for which no alternatives to antibiotics are available. When used properly, veterinary antibiotics are critical tools for managing disease in animals, preventing the spread of zoonotic diseases to humans, and helping ensure a safe food supply. MAH conducts studies and participates in surveillance programs to detect antibacterial resistance, engages in research to increase knowledge about the proper use of veterinary antibiotics, and provides clear guidelines to veterinarians, farmers, ranchers, and feed companies on the appropriate dosage, duration, and resistance management of our agents. In fact, many of these efforts within MAH dovetail with Merck's broader antimicrobial stewardship principles and align with similar programs supported by the Merck Human Health divisions of our company.

In case you're interested, I've shared in **Table 3** three examples showing how our colleagues within MAH are helping make the world a better place. To illustrate my point, I've limited these examples to my favorite animal. If you have not yet figured it out what animal this might be, shame on you. Clearly, you have not been paying attention. Of course, it is none other than my furry ally, the canine.

So, today, I'm thankful to all my wonderful colleagues within the MAH division for all they do to protect the welfare, livelihood, and wellbeing of our treasured, nonhuman friends. MAH has developed innovative products that have transformed modern veterinary medicine. The novel drugs and vaccines that MAH manufactures protect our pets, our farm animals, and our food chain. Unlike many other pharmaceutical companies, Merck has remained steadfast in our commitment to our animal health division. While big pharma seeks to spin off their veterinary divisions, Merck is content to invest further in this growing business, and, in turn, to continue to support the needs of pet owners, veterinarians, and farmers throughout the world. I'd like to acknowledge all our colleagues within MAH for all they do to address our medical needs. I'm also sincerely grateful to those at other companies, academic institutions, and public agencies that are broadly working towards advancing animal health. As an infectious disease physician, I recognize that animal health is critical to ensure the protection of human health. In my humble opinion, it is in Merck's best interest that we continue to do all we can to treat and prevent zoonotic diseases for the betterment of humanity.

In closing, I'd also like to take a moment to publicly wish Jango a wonderful 10th birthday. Of course, this milestone is also a salient reminder that he is no longer a puppy but rather 75 years of age in human years. Jango has been an amazing addition to the Kartsonis family. But, I don't want to leave you thinking he is perfect. He's far from it. Although he knows how to sit on command, Jango has never mastered the art of giving paw, despite repeated training and endless coaxing with doggie treats. Moreover, contrary to other dogs of his breed, he's never effectively retrieved a tennis ball, a newspaper, or anything else for that matter, again despite repeated training and endless coaxing with doggie treats. Also, Jango has never learned how to be a guard dog. For the most part, Golden Retrievers do not serve as reliable security systems—not only will they let a would-be thief into your home, they'll show the robber where we hide the family silver. Jango has, however, learned how to shed his hair everywhere in our house, and he finds great delight in rolling in whatever God-forsaken stench he can find in our backyard. He has also been known to frustrate Daisy and me by quitting on a walk.

Jango perfectly epitomizes what the American wit Ogden Nash once said about his own pet: "A door is what a dog is perpetually on the wrong side of."[19] So even though I previously mentioned that Jango rarely barks, he'll let out a hearty single yelp when he inexplicably finds himself on the wrong side of the door—usually at the critical juncture of an Eagles game or the climax of some action-packed movie. Sadly, our family has and will continue to accommodate his royal requests. In fact, we have so frequently opened the back door to our house to appease Jango that the door recently needed replacing. It's enough to make me want to SMH —that's "shake my head" for all the non-millennials out there.

All that said, I wouldn't replace Jango for the world. He has been, by far, the least complicated relationship I've ever had in my life. I am sincerely thankful each day for his endless love, steadfast resolve, and enduring companionship. I'm also extremely grateful to Sam for his persistence in requesting a family pet. Finally, I would be remiss if I did not show my gratitude to Daisy for cajoling me into bringing the checkbook to Princeton that fateful day some ten years ago.

---

19 From "A Dog's Best Friend Is His Illiteracy" in *The Private Dining Room* (1953)

Table 3. Three Concrete Examples of Merck Animal Health's Impact on Jango's Wellness

1. Many of us are familiar with human influenza viruses and the detrimental impact these can have on society. Well, dogs can also get influenza. The first cases of canine influenza virus (CIV) in the United States were reported in 2004. Caused by an H3N8 virus, influenza had s spread to dogs from horses and then spread quickly among various dog species. Eventually, a vaccine was developed and was given to dogs to prevent the infection. Then a massive outbreak of a new strain of CIV was reported in the spring of 2015. First detected in Chicago, the infection quickly spread and infected the canine population in over 26 states, often causing severe, debilitating disease, including fever, lethargy, persistent cough, and thick nasal discharge. Unlike the original CIV, this virus originated in birds and was spread to dogs. Merck worked with the academic community, including experts at the University of Wisconsin, to identify the cause of the virus (H3N2), helped develop educational materials to share with veterinarians and pet owners throughout the country, and quickly went to work to develop a vaccine. Within eight months of the virus' identification, MAH received conditional approval from the FDA for a new vaccine. Today, Merck markets a bivalent CIV vaccine (NOBIVAC® Canine Flu Bivalent) that covers both H3N8 and H3N2. How awesome is that!
2. Rabies is a significant infection in many developing parts of the world. On average, about 60 thousand people will die from rabies annually. Over 40 percent of those deaths occur in children and adolescents less than 15 years of age. Sadly, this equates to nearly 100 rabies deaths per day in the global pediatric population. As previously noted, rabies is a preventable infection, and Merck has developed a rabies vaccine that protects dogs, cats, and other animals from rabies. However, in the developing world where most cases of rabies occur, dogs are not routinely vaccinated. For this reason, MAH has joined the global fight against rabies by donating over one million doses of canine rabies vaccine to two key initiatives, the Afya Serengeti Project and Mission Rabies. The Afya Serengeti Project, which was founded more than two decades ago, has used Merck's NOBIVAC® vaccines to immunize domesticated dogs in Uganda, Tanzania, Malawi, Sri Lanka, and certain parts of India, helping to reduce canine rabies and the transmission

of rabies in humans via bites from rabid dogs. Mission Rabies is a program that is now entering its sixth year, with a focus on eliminating rabies in certain spots in India, where nearly a third of all rabies cases are observed. Merck donates nearly a quarter of a million doses of NOBIVAC® Rabies Vaccine each year to this project. In the past, Merck has even matched each purchased dose by pet owners in the US with an additional dose of vaccine in the developing world. Together with human vaccination, these efforts are going a long way towards meeting the 2030 Rabies Elimination Effort—it's about time we take a bite out of rabies.

3. Early on, I mentioned the microchip *Home Again®*, which Jango has embedded under his skin. This technology allows for Jango's microchip number or that of any dog or cat with a similar microchip to be registered in a national database and identified if he is ever lost. The program works. Over 15 million registered pets are included in the database. In 2016 alone, over 240,000 missing pets were reunited with their owners. To date, the program has reunited over two million pets with their rightful owners. Back in November, my son Sam—the one who really wanted Jango—found a dog without a tag aimlessly trotting along a busy street. Knowing that Jango possesses a microchip, Sam guessed that the lost dog might have one as well. Sam and a fellow student somehow corralled the dog into their car and brought him to the local veterinary office, where they discovered that the dog did indeed have a microchip. Fortunately, the dog was reconnected with his owner later that evening, capping off another success story. Reunited, and it feels so good!

17 Commending Those Who Keep Calm and Carry on *(April 25, 2019)*

For this week's *Thankful Thursday* segment, I'd like to lionize those oft-underappreciated heroes who educate and campaign publicly for immunization. Although Merck's legacy in vaccine development is unquestionable, today is not a day that I'll praise my Merck colleagues who develop, manufacture, and commercialize vaccines. Rather, I'm focusing this week's commendation on those external crusaders who lead the charge in advocating for vaccination, even in the face of dissent, hesitancy, and misinformation.

The incredible innovation the world has witnessed in the last 100 years can be expressed by a single word—mind-boggling. The twentieth century was simply remarkable in terms of its unprecedented rate of technological advances, scientific innovation, and societal improvements. During that time, the automobile and the airplane emerged as safe, highly-efficient vehicles to facilitate personal travel on land or in the air. Heck, our capabilities to push the limit of human travel even culminated in several successful trips to the moon, an unparalleled testimony to human ingenuity and courage. Over the last century, we've also learned to harness the sun, the wind, and even the atom to generate energy. Consequentially, that same energy helps to power our twentieth century technological innovations, such as the radio, television, personal computers, and cell phones. In turn, we have become increasingly connected to our rapidly-changing world. We can now watch endless reruns of any of the more than 650 episodes of the *Simpsons* on our iPads while sitting comfortably on a plane. Or we can download the latest pop hit from Jessica Simpson on our iPhones while riding in a car. All these inventions improve our connectivity with the world while enhancing personal wellbeing and satisfaction. Yet I would be hard pressed to say any of these inventions, despite their efficiency, convenience, and entertainment value, have had an impact on human health or life expectancy. In fact, some would argue our technological advances have occasionally been nefariously repurposed, leading to the advent of biological terrorism, computerized military drones, and nuclear weaponry.

Nevertheless, we keep calm and carry on.

If we want to champion human longevity, we need to turn our attention to the medical innovations of the last century. By the end of the nineteenth century, the average life expectancy was 49 years. Fast forwarding to the end of the twentieth century, we find that the mean life expectancy had increased nearly three decades to 78 years. Although it is hard to ascribe this increase to a single medical advance, it is probably fair to say that that three factors were integral: technological advances in nutritional and medical care, antibiotics, and vaccines. First, nutritional advancements, such as refrigeration and vitamin fortification foods, have been crucial. Medical technological advances, such as magnetic resonance imaging, improved blood testing, and routine cancer screening have helped facilitate this achievement. Even procedural advances in areas such as modern surgery and organ transplants warrant particular acclaim. Yet, for effective surgery or transplants to occur, we need advances in antibacterial therapy. Since Alexander Fleming's initial discovery of penicillin in 1928, more than ten unique classes of antibacterial agents have been licensed, providing cures to microbial scourges that cause serious infections such as pneumonia, urinary tract infections, and blood stream infections. However, most individuals would never reach the age to need surgery, transplants, or antibiotic therapy if it weren't for the third advance—mass vaccination. As we discussed in a prior *Thankful Thursday* segment, the first vaccine targeting smallpox was developed by Dr. Edward Jenner in 1796, when he vaccinated a neighbor's child with the cowpox virus. In the nineteenth century, progress made by Louis Pasteur and others led to the development of additional vaccines against four other human or animal targets: rabies, typhoid fever, cholera, and anthrax. However, vaccination did not really hit its stride until the early 1950s. At that time, the advancement of a combination vaccine against three deadly diseases (diphtheria, pertussis, and tetanus (DPT)) and the Salk polio vaccine breakthrough were the true impetus that heralded the birth of modern vaccinology (**Figure 14**). These efforts catapulted individuals like Merck's own Maurice Hilleman to pursue a wide array of pediatric vaccine targets, starting with a live attenuated measles vaccine in 1963. By the end of the twentieth century, vaccines would be developed and licensed for a large cadre of bacterial and viral targets.

I'm not exaggerating when I proclaim that vaccines are one of the highlights of scientific innovation and probably the greatest invention for public health. The impact that vaccine development had on public health in the twentieth century has been well chronicled by scientists, epidemiologists, and medical historians. As a case in point, the United States Center for Disease Control and Prevention (CDC) published a fascinating article in the April 1999 edition of *Morbidity and Mortality Weekly Report* (MMWR); the report highlights the near-miraculous progress in vaccine development, showing reductions in vaccine-preventable diseases between 1900 and 1999. If we just consider the nine bacterial and viral targets for which a vaccine was routinely given in pediatric patients by 1990—smallpox, diphtheria, pertussis, tetanus, poliomyelitis, measles, mumps, rubella, and *Haemophilus influenzae* B—we can paint a clearer picture showing how vaccines fundamentally transformed pediatric health by the end of the twentieth century. Take smallpox: In the early 1900s, about 50,000 smallpox cases occurred each year in the US, and an active infection with a major form of this disease was associated with about 1,500 deaths annually. Mass immunization with a small pox vaccine in the twentieth century ultimately led to the virus's eradication by 1977. Although the smallpox vaccine is the only vaccine whose use has been discontinued because of disease eradication, the number of cases for each of the other eight targets has also been significantly reduced. The MMWR article shows that vaccines reduced morbidity for each of these eight diseases by 96 percent. How amazing is that! As former CDC Director William Foege said: "Vaccines are the tugboats of preventive health."[20]

Today, we now have 12 vaccines that are routinely recommended to pediatric patients by the CDC's Advisory Committee of Immunization Practices (ACIP). These vaccines target 16 different bacterial and viral diseases. Fourteen of those targets are protected by immunization in the first few years of life, while another two are protected by vaccines

---

20 Dr Foege frequently says this in public talks. See https://www.pbs.org/wgbh/rxforsurvival/series/champions/william_h_foege.html.

administered in preadolescence. Several other vaccines are specifically recommended by the ACIP for use in adults. Hence, it is only fitting we take a moment today to contemplate the incredible healthcare impact that such vaccines have afforded to humanity worldwide.

Why is today a good time to take stock in these achievements?

The last week of April is World Immunization Week (WIW), a global public health campaign endorsed by the World Health Organization (WHO) to raise awareness of the importance of global vaccination. The hope is that this initiative will spur individuals and parents to increase rates of immunization against vaccine-preventable diseases around the world. The 2019 WIW commemoration celebrates the seventh anniversary of this important undertaking. This year's theme is focused on **Protected Together: Vaccines Work!**—no truer statement has been spoken. Such an effort is critical because our mission to vaccinate the world's pediatric population is not complete: Sadly, one in every five infants in the world, mostly in low and middle-income countries, do not receive basic vaccinations. In other words, more than 22 million infants worldwide are not protected from some basic diseases like measles, mumps, and polio. How can it be that it has been 50 years since our first trek to the moon, and yet basic vaccinations are still not a full reality for the world's most precious commodity—its own children?

OK, I need to remind myself again to keep calm and carry on.

Today, in commemoration of WIW, I'd like to use my *Thankful Thursday* segment to praise those individuals who courageously carry the torch for vaccination. Let's start with a few vaccine advocates that warrant our praise.

In 2018, many famous individuals were laid to rest, including President George W.H. Bush and First Lady Barbara Bush, Senator John McCain, singer Aretha Franklin, physicist Stephen Hawking, and the UN Secretary General Kofi Annan. Did anybody take a moment to honor the passing of Betty Bumpers? Probably not, but she probably was the most influential of them all. As the wife of Arkansas governor Dale Bumpers, Betty initiated a statewide campaign to vaccinate all of Arkansas's children. In a campaign entitled *Every Child by '74,* Betty corralled her state government, medical professional organizations, and Arkansan citizens to help deliver immunizations to their youth. By 1975, Arkansas had transformed its statewide rates of childhood immunizations from one of the lowest to the one of the highest in the nation. But Betty's crusade did not stop in Arkansas. When her husband became a US Senator in 1975, Betty pursued a nationwide program for immunization. Enlisting the support of First Lady Rosalynn Carter, Betty began a campaign to convince every state to require its children to be immunized prior to entering school. By 1979, the campaign had achieved its goal of having all 50 US states enact legislation requiring immunization prior to school entry. But the crusade was still not over. In the early 1990s, Betty and Rosalynn took this campaign one step further to create an organization called *Every Child by Two* to ensure that immunizations are given to preschool children, as they also carry risk of developing vaccine-preventable diseases. By 2012, each US state had achieved over 90 percent immunization rates for DTP, polio, measles, mumps, rubella, and Hepatitis B in toddlers and infants. In 2014, it was estimated that the number of US children that had received no vaccinations at all was reduced to less than 1 percent.

Other living advocates also deserve acclaim. Dr. Paul Offit, a pediatrician at Children's Hospital of Pennsylvania, has been a true stalwart to the vaccination cause. When he was five years old, he spent time in a polio ward recovering from clubfoot surgery. The sobering experience of witnessing children suffering from a preventable disease made him determine to help the vulnerable youth of the world. Offit became a preeminent pediatrician and well-respected vaccine researcher. His research efforts led to the development of the oral, pentavalent rotavirus vaccine, which Merck has licensed and is on the current list of ACIP-recommended vaccines for US infants. However, Offit is probably more known for his unrelenting advocacy of vaccination. Over the last two decades, he has become one of leading advocates for childhood immunizations. He has written numerous books on the topic, never shying away from taking a hard line on the importance of childhood health. Offit has spoken publicly on the importance of vaccination, appearing on popular daytime and nighttime television shows to provide cogent, scientific-based arguments in favor of vaccination. Such fervent advocacy for public health has made him a target of much animosity from those who oppose vaccination. Despite heaps of hate mail and the occasional death threat, Offit remains undeterred in his pursuit of science and public health. I laud Offit and the many other living advocates (such as Stanley Plotkin, Bill Schaffner, Deborah Wexler, Peter Hotez, and

Julie Bloom) for their determined spirit and unyielding pursuit of this important cause.

It's not just the individual advocates who warrant our ovations. Non-profit organizations such as The Immunization Project and Immunization Action Coalition provide the lay public and the medical community important resources at the local, statewide, and national level to help educate individuals, parents, and providers on the critical importance of timely vaccination. Many of these organizations also advance public policy in support of the vaccination cause. Parent-led organizations, such as *Voices for Vaccines*, provide parents reliable, evidence-based information that helps promote immunization. The Voices for Vaccines blog entitled *Parents Who Vax* provide a public forum in which pro-vaccination parents can share their personal stories, offer support, and explain their rationale for the cause.

Finally, I would be remiss if I did not hail those tireless organizations that help to distribute vaccines around the world, especially to children in low and middle-income countries that need it the most. Let's start with the Global Alliance for Vaccines and Immunization (GAVI), which is a public-private partnership whose sole mission is to create equal access of vaccines to the poorest children in the world. Founded in 2000, GAVI has helped to save numerous children's lives by providing lower income countries with access to vaccines. I thought it might help to share some of the eye-opening statistics to illustrate the GAVI success story. Since its inception, GAVI has immunized more than 700 million children against a variety of infections, and the annual number of immunizations continues to grow. Just in 2017 alone, over 65 million children were immunized against everything from DPT, measles, polio, meningococcus, pneumococcus, *H. influenzae* B, rotavirus, and human papillomavirus. Through the support of organizations such as WHO, United Nations Children's Fund (UNICEF), The World Bank, and the Bill and Melinda Gates Foundation, GAVI's reach has likely averted ten million deaths. Amazingly, they reach close to 80 percent of the children in these poorest countries. Fortunately, the GAVI Board and GAVI Secretariat hope to close the gap in the coming five years for every child that they currently do not reach.

But GAVI is not alone in this fight. Organizations such as Global Polio Eradication Initiative (GPEI) have taken on a specific immunization mission. In a public-private partnership supported by national governments, the WHO, CDC, UNICEF, and Rotary International, GPEI has furthered the cause of polio eradication. GPEI has been working to eradicate polio for the last 20 years. This initiative was first conceived in 1988, at a time when polio occurred in over 350,000 people worldwide and the disease was still endemic in most parts of the developing world. Since then, over 20 million volunteers affiliated with GPEI have helped reduced polio incidence by 99.99 percent. Over 16 million more people today are walking and 1.5 million are alive because GPEI brought an oral polio vaccine to the infants in these needy nations. In 2018, only 33 cases of polio were reported in Afghanistan, Pakistan, and Nigeria. Now, GPEI's work is not easy. Nor is it without risk. In the countries where they work, vociferous opposition to their humanitarian efforts exists. Many of their volunteers have been verbally attacked or physically abused, and some have even lost their lives for the mission. But GPEI perseveres because they know their cause is admirable, just, and worthwhile. Much like the WHO and Medicins sans Frontieres (MsF) workers who face hostility in the Democratic Republic of Congo when they distribute the Ebola vaccine, the GPEI staff continue to distribute the polio vaccine.

So, today, I express my gratitude to all those who support global immunization. Whether it's the individual advocates who advance the mission or the public organizations that disseminate evidence-based information on vaccines or the organizations such as GAVI, GPEI, WHO, and MsF who distribute vaccines, the world is in a better place because of these efforts. As we awake this morning, let's commemorate WIW by thanking those pro-vaccine leaders who help make the world a better place because of their diligent efforts.

In closing, let me add an interesting historical tidbit. Eighty years ago the government of the United Kingdom issued a motivational poster to raise the morale of the British public as the country prepared to enter World War II. Addressing the stoicism of the Brits, whose stiff upper lip mentality had helped them brave political storms, World War I, and dreary weather, the poster was not elaborate; it depicted a small picture of the royal crown and five simple words. So it is appropriate that I finish this segment with the same advice to those who are rallying to vaccinate humanity:

KEEP
CALM
AND
CARRY
ON

18 The Bold and Brilliant Beginning of the Biologics Business *(May 2, 2019)*

For this week's *Thankful Thursday* segment, I'd like to express my gratitude to the legacy of biologics. Biologics are derived from living entities, and these products include vaccines, monoclonal antibodies, blood and blood components, somatic cells and tissues, gene therapy, and recombinant proteins. Contrary to common belief, Merck's foray into biologics did not begin with the recent introduction of our monoclonal business or even our long-standing tradition in vaccine development. Long before pembrolizumab, bezlotoxumab, the multivalent human papillomavirus vaccine, and the combination measles/mumps/rubella vaccine came to market, Merck was developing biologics to address a variety of interesting conditions. The remarkable story that inspired our company's venture into a highly productive vaccine business and our recent monoclonal antibody initiatives started nearly 130 years ago in the City of Brotherly Love. Today I'll do my best to share this fascinating story in all its rightful glory.

But before we talk about Merck's ancestral roots in Philadelphia, I'd like to begin this tale in the lovely city of Louisville, Kentucky. Since 1875, the Kentucky Derby has been an annual event held on the first Saturday in May. Affectionately coined the "Most Exciting Two Minutes in Sports," the Kentucky Derby features 3-year old horses galloping rapidly around a 1.25-mile dirt racetrack at beautiful Churchill Downs. Ripe in tradition, this race represents the first leg of the American

Triple Crown; the colt or filly that is draped in a bed of roses at the end of the Kentucky Derby has the privilege of traveling north to attempt to win the other two legs, at the Preakness Stakes in Baltimore and the Belmont Stakes in New York. This weekend, over 150,000 attendees will don their preppy (loud) outfits and colorful, oversized hats to attend the Derby. They will patiently wait hour after hour for the featured race to start, all the while sipping mint juleps, eating burgoo, and singing folk songs that would bring a wry smile to the dour face of Daniel Boone. Despite two world wars, the Great Depression, and other national tragedies, the Kentucky Derby has never been cancelled—it serves as an enduring, fun fixture in America's relatively short history. Even the dainty Queen Elizabeth II let down her guard to attend the festivities on her trek to the United States in 2007. Although I've never attended this 145-year old event, the Derby remains a feature on my bucket list. Alas, I will not be attending the 2019 festivities, but I will be watching this Saturday at 6:50 PM to see if anyone can break the 1:59 record set by Secretariat in 1973. I suggest you don't miss it either!

Living near Philly, I'd probably cheer for any of the fillies in the 145th Kentucky Derby—but, sadly, it's an all-male race this year. So, I think I'll be rooting for Improbable, well, because sometimes being cast an underdog is a welcomed opportunity. Indeed, I've selected Improbable because I'm from Philadelphia, and the name reminds of the Eagles improbable run to the Super Bowl Championship in 2018.

As my mind gravitates from horses to Philadelphia, I'm left to ponder Merck's legacy to all things equestrian and the city so fondly called the Birthplace of America. We've also heard the tale about our company's founder, George F. Merck, and how he arrived at New York City from Germany in 1891 to start the Merck subsidiary of his German family's pharmaceutical business. I shared many of those details with you in a prior *Thankful Thursday* segment, in which I lauded my wonderful home state of New Jersey. I'll come back to George F. Merck in a future segment as well. Indeed, most pharmaceutical companies in the US have their roots in the New York/New Jersey area, but there's a part of the Merck history closely attached to Philadelphia. Our company's affiliation to this historic city on the Delaware River is often overlooked in the lore of our pharmaceutical history. Fortunately, there's one biologic that Merck still produces, with the help of our equine companions, that helps keep the historic memory alive.

So, as I launch into a description of our oldest surviving biologic, I'll kindly ask that you pardon my indulgence by joining me on a trip back in time to the late nineteenth century and the burgeoning industrial city of Philadelphia. I'm setting the time machine back 130 years to 1889 and the location to the corner of 18th and Market Street and the roots of Merck's biologic business. Not surprisingly, you'll now find a Starbucks café at this site. But, long before baristas started concocting Grande-sized Caramel Macchiatos on these premises, the staff at the Old Simes Retail Pharmacy, which was located at this site in 1889, were concocting a cadre of medical potions, tinctures, syrups, sodas, and antiseptics—all designed to treat a variety of ailments and conditions afflicting Philadelphians in the late nineteenth century. Amid the Industrial Revolution, the poor labor practices in factories, mass immigration, especially from southern European countries, and the overcrowded living conditions in the city slums had transformed Philadelphia and other large cities into petri dishes for infectious diseases such as smallpox, tuberculosis, and diphtheria. In the late nineteenth century, Philadelphia was rife with two things: infectious ailments and small pharmacies that sold products to treat these ailments. In the late 1880s, a 21-year old pharmacy graduate named Henry Kimball Mulford purchased the old pharmacy retail store on 18th and Market Streets. With the financial backing of a friend, Milton Campbell, Henry Mulford also purchased a compressed tablet machine and began expanding the offerings at the small pharmacy shop, which he ultimately transformed into the H.K. Mulford Company.

Mulford and Campbell were true entrepreneurs looking for the next great pharmaceutical offering. They were familiar with the evolving medical literature heralding the successes of Louis Pasteur and Robert Koch in advancing the fields of vaccinology and bacteriology, respectively. By the early 1890s, a few of Koch's colleagues in Berlin had made an astounding discovery regarding antisera. One of Koch's proteges, Emil von Behring, and his Japanese postdoctoral fellow, Shibasaburo Kitasato, had discovered a toxin-destroying agent that was derived from serum collected from animals artificially-exposed to low levels of bacterial toxins. These scientists had shown that a treatment against diphtheria could be developed from repeated exsanguinations of the blood from horses following prior exposure to gradually increasing doses of the bacterium. Unbeknownst to those discoverers, the protection being afforded by this antitoxin sera was equine-generated antibodies against the diphtheria toxin.

Normally, in the absence of antibodies against its exotoxin, the *C. diphtheriae* bacterium can invade human lungs and produce a fatal toxin that kills the epithelial cells lining the respiratory tract. As this necrotic tissue accumulates, a thick, gray pseudo-membrane narrows the nasal and respiratory cavities, leading to difficulty swallowing and eventual asphyxiation. At that time, the only known treatment for a severe case of diphtheria was a tracheotomy, which was a technically complicated procedure. Even after successful surgery, the bacterial toxins could still lead to cardiac, renal, or neurological organ failure and eventual death. The antitoxin technology, which Behring shared with Dr. William Park and his colleagues at the New York's Public Health Department, was acknowledged to be a crucial achievement. This significant advance did not escape the eye of the H. K. Mulford executives. They decided to go all in to see if this most drastic innovation in antitoxin production could be successfully scaled up for broader use by the afflicted public.

So, what H.K. Mulford did next was simply brilliant and changed the trajectory of their small company.

Mulford and Campbell decided the first thing they needed to do was build the intellectual know-how and technical capacity to produce antitoxins. So, they did what I've routinely done when I need to hire someone. They travelled a few blocks west on Market Street and recruited the best clinicians, researchers, and veterinarians from the prestigious University of Pennsylvania (UP) complex. As the oldest medical school in the United States, UP was known for its medical brainpower and veterinary expertise. Scientists such as Drs. Joseph MacFarland, Clarence Lincoln, Leonard Pearson, John Reichel, and John Adams were hired by Mulford, and they rapidly learned and perfected the technology of antisera production from Dr. Park at the New York Public Health Department. Dr. Park obliged these eager H.K. Mulford employees for the sake of improving public health. Mulford and Campbell also acquired the space needed to develop antitoxin. They secured a 200-acre parcel of land approximately eight miles south of Philadelphia in the town on Glenolden (just north of the present Philadelphia International Airport), where they invested heavily in building the stables and farms needed to quarter the assembly of horses, cows, sheep, and other animals which would naturally produce their antitoxin and other biological products. They also erected separate research laboratories and manufacturing edifices needed to perform the culture, sterilization, processing, and standardization steps, the latter of which was done for many years in close conjunction with the labs at UP.

The race was on between Mulford and a Detroit-based company, Park Davis, to develop the first commercial supply of the antitoxin. Mulford had the scientific expertise in his corner and won the race. By 1895, H.K. Mulford commenced the commercial production of the first antitoxin against diphtheria. In short order, the firm was also developing antisera against a host of other infectious ailments, including tetanus, anthrax, brucellosis, and streptococcal infections. Mulford and Campbell also ventured into vaccine development and helped supply much of the northeastern United States with the smallpox vaccine. In due time, they developed other human and veterinary vaccines to tackle conditions such as rabies, typhoid, anthrax, and black leg disease (a deadly infection in cows). They even cultivated large gardens on their land in Glenolden to harvest natural products, such as digitalis, which is derived from the foxglove flower (**Figure 15**).

In 1898 Mulford hired a young aspiring physician-turned-chemist named Albert Barnes from the UP. Dr. Barnes had previously studied in Berlin at the Koch Institute, and after being employed by Mulford, he returned to Heidelberg where he honed his skill in chemistry. While there, he visited many museums and gained an appreciation for the fine arts. Upon his return to the US, he ventured off on his own with another German chemist to create a silver nitrate antiseptic (Argyrol®). This product was administered to prevent neonatal blindness caused by *N. gonorrhoeae* (the etiological agent that causes gonorrhea) and to treat other ophthalmologic infections. The business blossomed, and Barnes used his newly-found wealth to have a high school colleague travel back to Europe to purchase paintings from French artists such as Renoir, Matisse, Cezanne, and Picasso. He adorned his home in Merion, Pennsylvania, with these masterpieces, as well as the works from other aspiring European, Chinese, and Native American artists. After his 1951 death from a tragic auto collision, his treasured collection was opened to the public. Eventually, much to the chagrin of many local Pennsylvanians and against the previously stated wishes of Barnes and his surviving family, the entire exhibit was moved to Philadelphia, where a museum to the Barnes collection was erected in

2012. If you've never been to the Barnes Museum, I'd encourage you to visit the fascinating display of art at the gallery on the Avenue of the Arts in downtown Philly.

While Barnes went his artistic way, the H.K. Mulford Company flourished. By 1915, H.K. Mulford employed over 1,000 employees, possessed 1,500 horses, and established offices in all the major cities across the United States and one in Canada. Two specific events further solidified their success. First, in advance of President Woodrow Wilson's decision to join the World War I effort in 1917, the US government secured a substantial supply of Mulford's diphtheria antitoxin and other antisera/vaccine products. As a result, the revenues for the company nearly tripled in a span of a decade. Secondly, in the winter of 1925, a near-tragic circumstance propelled the Mulford name into the national spotlight. At that time, *The New York Times* publicized the saga of the remote, snowed-in town of Nome, Alaska, which had been stricken by an epidemic of diphtheria. The closest supplier of antitoxin was based at the end of the Alaskan railroad, in the town of Nenana. Following a desperate telegram plea from the local physician, Alaskan authorities secured the support of a chain of dogsled mushers to transfer Mulford's antitoxin the 674 miles across the rugged, snowy terrain from Nenana to Nome. Fortunately, the antitoxin arrived in time and, following its thawing, was distributed to the Nome inhabitants. The first successful cold chain supply of a Merck product was realized! Today, this success story is commemorated with the annual running of the Iditarod Trail Sled Dog Race, a 46-year-old event that is held each March. Like the Kentucky Derby, this sled race is a popular annual sporting event. However, mint juleps are aptly replaced with steaming cups of hot cocoa, and those elaborate hats worn at the Derby have been supplanted by practical ski caps.

Mulford's astounding success in mass-producing antitoxin led the company to experiment with similar techniques that use animal sera to combat non-infectious conditions. In 1895, a French scientist at the Pasteur Institute had developed the first antivenom against the bite of an Indian cobra. Much like antitoxin production, antivenom is produced by injecting small amounts of venom into a domesticated animal, such as a horse or goat. The antibodies produced in the blood of these animals are then harvested and processed following the necessary concentration and purification steps. Just as an antitoxin can only target the toxin of a single bacterium, antivenom can often only combat the venom of a single animal species. Despite advances in the antivenom field by others, including experts in Brazil who had trained at the Pasteur Institute, no one in the United States had truly perfected the skill. So the scientists at H.K. Mulford partnered with Brazilian experts to collect venom from a variety of species of snakes and to commence the mass-production of antivenom against the North American pit vipers—rattlesnakes, moccasins, and copperheads. This product, Antivenin Nearctic Crotalidae, was launched in 1927 as the first antivenom sold in the United States. In due time, the company also developed antivenom against South American pit vipers.

By this time, H.K. Mulford had become an acquisition target of larger pharmaceutical companies interested in venturing into research, particularly for their proficiency in antisera and vaccine technology. In 1929, a larger distribution company, Sharp & Dohme, acquired H.K. Mulford Company and its biologic enterprise. Sharp & Dohme proceeded to expand the biologic initiatives that had been ongoing for over 30 years in Glenolden. In 1936 they introduced the first antivenom against the black widow spider, *Latrodectus mactans.* Sharp & Dohme continued antivenom and vaccine production, and it expanded its footprint with the purchase of a large tract of land in West Point, Pennsylvania, in 1952.

By 1952, antitoxin serum was being supplanted by vaccines and progress in antibacterial research. Besides the smallpox vaccine, Sharp and Dohme was manufacturing a variety of antibiotics, including sulfonamides and new formulations of penicillin. In 1949 a combination vaccine against diphtheria, pertussis, and tetanus (DPT), was introduced, obviating the need for the Mulford/Sharp & Dohme antisera against these same conditions. The global successes in vaccinology propelled another pharmaceutical company, Merck and Co., Inc., to seek a partner that could help expand its own growing anti-infective market and support its interest in immunization technology. In 1953, the merger between Merck and Sharp & Dohme resulted in Merck, Sharp & Dohme (MSD). In short order, MSD began expanding its research efforts in vaccine development at the newly acquired West Point site. Maurice Hilleman would join MSD in 1957 to help promote vaccines, and as radio broadcaster Paul Harvey used to say, you know the rest of the story.

For many years thereafter, Merck was the sole provider of antivenom products against the bites of snakes and the black widow spider. Even as this business waned and was surpassed by more affordable options, Merck maintained several stallions on the West Point site to produce these products. When I first joined Merck in 2000, I would travel, on occasion, to West Point for a meeting or to discuss programs with my research and discovery colleagues. I always parked my vehicle in the lot adjacent to Entrance 3 so I could walk past the pasture where the horses gracefully grazed amidst the office buildings on the West Point campus. Today, other antivenom suppliers have commercially introduced a sheep-derived, polyvalent antivenom to neutralize the venom from North American pit vipers (Cro-Fab®), so Merck has discontinued snake antivenoms. However, Merck remains the United States' sole supplier for antivenom against the black widow spider. Individuals who succumb to an adult, female black widow spider bite are privy to develop latrodectism, an intense, unsettling illness accompanied by sweating, muscle pain, rigidity (especially in the abdominal musculature), vomiting, and goosebumps. On rare occasion, the condition can progress to muscle breakdown, inflammation of heart muscle, and even death, especially in vulnerable children, the elderly, pregnant women, and those with significant cardiac comorbidities. The antivenom is administered intravenously, often with analgesics and muscle relaxants, to help alleviate further injury caused by the spider's venom.

So, today, I'm thankful for Merck's rich, illustrious history in biologics. Our nearly 130-year history of maintaining an unwavering pursuit of biologic discoveries has allowed us to introduce biologics that tackle cancer, infection, and immunologic conditions. Those efforts continue today in the research work we pursue in places such as Rahway, South San Francisco, Boston, London, and, of course, West Point. With regard to West Point, I'd caution against searching for the horses that supply the antivenom against the black widow spider. They now graze on a farm in Lancaster, Pennsylvania, hopefully in a more tranquil, less crowded landscape. Our equine companions may be physically gone from the West Pont site, but their legacy lives on in biologic products such as pembrolizumab, bezlotoxumab, our many vaccines, and, of course, *Latrodectus mactans* antivenom (**Figure 16**).

So, when you tune into the Kentucky Derby this Saturday evening, take a moment to thank our diligent corporate ancestors at H.K. Mulford Company, who had the vision and courage to develop and commercialize our first biologic. They've taught us one relevant lesson:

If you want to be a relevant player in the biologic business, you better not monkey around, but it is perfectly appropriate to horse around.

P.S. Much of what I relayed to you today can be found in a wonderful book entitled *Networks of Innovation: Vaccine Development at Merck, Sharp and Dohme, and Mulford* (1895-1995). The authors are a married couple, Louis Galambos and Jane Eliot Sewell. Unfortunately, Sewell died at the age of 42 when she was struck by a truck while on vacation in Santa Fe in 2002. Galambos continues to teach American business history as an emeritus professor at Johns Hopkins University.

19 Merck's Magnanimous Mission to Minimize Maternal Mortality *(May 9, 2019)*

For this week's *Thankful Thursday* segment, I'd like to express my gratitude to our company's humanitarian mission to ensure that that every child born into this world is given the love and care of a mother. Our company has embraced a daunting task of attempting to reduce the world's rate of maternal mortality. In doing so, Merck envisions a world where no mother perishes while giving the gift of life. So, today, it is only fitting that I laud our 10-year, $500 million initiative to save the lives of all new moms, *Merck for Mothers*.

In three days, the second Sunday in May will be upon us. Here in the United States, as well as in 95 other countries in the world, we will celebrate Mother's Day, a Sunday honoring all mothers, living or deceased. In turn, the holiday also commemorates the power and influence of motherhood, the unyielding bond between a mother and her children, and the immense impact of mothers in our society. Our young country has observed this annual practice of showing appreciation for motherhood for the last 105 years, following the formal proclamation of a nationwide Mother's Day celebration by President Woodrow Wilson in 1914.

Like biologics, the Mother's Day celebration has its roots in Philadelphia. The first biologic—an antitoxin against *Clostridium diphtheriae*—was licensed by H.K Mulford Company, a Philadelphia-based pharmaceutical company, in the late 1890s. Similarly,

Philadelphia played an instrumental role in first Mother's Day celebration.

Now, some of you reading this might acknowledge that it is only fitting that Philadelphia be closely tied to the birth of this celebration. In fact, before I uncovered the true story behind Mother's Day, I conceived at least four reasons why Philadelphia might have such a tight connection to this commemorative holiday:

1. As the birthplace of the US, Philadelphia is essentially the mother of our nation. It was in this colonial town that, in 1776, the Declaration of Independence was formally signed and publicly announced. The labor of love of birthing a new nation was indeed a courageous, patriotic act. Similarly, motherhood, like apple pie, is an American ideal. So, one could imagine numerous ways that Pennsylvania's largest city also served as a maternal symbol to spur President Wilson to pursue a celebration for all the mothers in our nation.
2. For a long time, Philadelphia has served as the motherland of all inventions. As the home of our nation's first bona fide inventor, Benjamin Franklin, the city has been witness to many of his creations, such as the lightning rod, the Franklin stove, the bifocal glasses, and even swim fins. Mothers dedicate themselves to educating their young, caring for their ill offspring, and putting out fires on the home front, so it only seems just that the city that supported the first subscription library, the first medical school, and the first volunteer fire department would have some intricate connection to motherhood. Even the first pencil with an eraser was invented in Philly, as a testament to what our own mothers taught us all along: it is never too late to correct an ill-founded error.
3. The world entrusts our mothers (along with our fathers) to help raise well-suited, healthy children. Hence, it is indeed appropriate that the city that founded the first US institution of pediatric care, the Children's Hospital of Philadelphia (CHOP), would have a stake in the first Mother's Day celebration. Back in 1855, Dr. Francis West Lewis started CHOP, after visiting the Great Ormond Street Hospital for Sick Children in London. Since that time, CHOP has become a world-renowned pioneer in pediatric care, recognized for providing superb medical support to ailing children. Not surprisingly, the first neonatal care unit was opened after World

War II by CHOP's chairman and eventual US Surgeon General, Dr. C. Everett Koop. How fitting is it that this cosmopolitan city at the forefront of pediatric care would have a stake in the first Mother's Day!

4. As Mother's Day is a celebration filled with bouquets (it's the second busiest holiday for florists behind Valentine's Day), one might imagine that the municipality's love for flowers would help solidify Philadelphia's role in the Mother's Day celebration. Since 1827, Philadelphia has served as the home of the Pennsylvania Horticultural Society, an organization that has sponsored the annual Philadelphia Flower Show. Now in its 190th year, the Philadelphia Flower Show is the world's largest gathering of florists, gardeners, and all those claiming to have a green thumb. In a town that also loves its green-cladded Eagles, it seems only just that the Mother's Day celebration would have first sprouted in Philadelphia.

Any of these four reasons might offer some rationale as to why Philadelphia is so attached to the Mother's Day celebration, but none are technically correct. So, how exactly did the City of *Brotherly* Love transform itself into city of *Motherly* Love?

The real story traces back to the middle of the nineteenth century. At that time, an upstanding American citizen named Anne Reeves Jarvis founded a social activist group, the Mother's Day Workers Club (MDWC), in her hometown of Grafton, West Virginia. As a mother who witnessed the death of 7 of her 11 children in infancy or early childhood, Jarvis used the forum to educate young West Virginian women on how to properly care for the health and wellbeing of their offspring. After witnessing the carnage and devastation of the Civil War, Jarvis transformed the group's mission into one of reconciliation. West Virginia was a unique state wherein many families had both Union and Confederate ties. In the war's aftermath, Jarvis's MDWC helped unify West Virginians still divided by the horrific consequences of the Civil War. In her community, she ardently promoted the Mother's Day Proclamation, which was first issued by Julia Ward Howe, an early abolitionist and suffragette. This petition, written in 1870, was

Howe's pacifist appeal to all women for national and global peace: "In this day of progress, in this century of light, the ambition of rulers has been allowed to barter the dear interests of domestic life for the bloody exchanges of the battle-field. Thus men have done. Thus men will do. But women need no longer be made a party to proceedings which fill the globe with grief and horror."[21] In 1872, Howe advocated unsuccessfully for the first Mother's Day for Peace celebration. Similarly, Jarvis advocated the same with her MDWC group in 1876, without much luck. Although neither Howe or Jarvis were successful in their Mother's Day pursuit, Jarvis' ninth child, Anna Marie Jarvis, kept the flame alive. Heeding her mother's belief that women deserve equal educational opportunities, the young Anna attended college at what is now Mary Baldwin University. Upon receiving a two-year diploma, she moved to Philadelphia where she became the first female Literary and Advertising Editor at the Fidelity Mutual Life Insurance Company. As Anna's mother aged and become frailer, she too moved to Philadelphia to be cared for by Anna. Her mother eventually died in Anna's company on May 9, 1905.

Upon her mother's death, Anna decided to follow through on her mother's wish for a day dedicated to motherhood. She hoped to honor her own mother by establishing a day for those persons who have done more for you than anyone in the world. For the next ten years, she pleaded with local, state, and federal authorities to help advocate for this commemoration. Her initial letters to the US Congress, President Theodore Roosevelt, and popular constituents such as Mark Twain failed to move the tide in her favor. Congress formally rejected a Mother's Day resolution in 1908, noting somewhat flippantly that if such a proclamation were issued it would also eventually lead to a Mother's-in-Law Day. It is sad, but not surprising, to witness how such traits of immaturity and ineptitude have continued to haunt Congressional leaders throughout the centuries.

Nevertheless, Anna persisted.

By the third anniversary of her mother's death, she had convinced a local Philadelphian friend and prosperous business owner, John Wanamaker, to assist in commissioning a formal event in celebration

21 From the "Appeal to Womanhood throughout the World," also known later as the Mother's Day Proclamation, written in 1870 in a pacifistic response to the devastation of the American Civil War and the Franco-Prussian War

of motherhood. On Sunday, May 10, 1908, the first observance of Mother's Day was held in two towns: Grafton, West Virginia, and Philadelphia, Pennsylvania. In honor of her mother's favorite flower, Anna handed out red carnations to those with living mothers and white carnations to those with deceased mothers. With the financial backing of Wanamaker and other local luminaries, Anna was able to move the legislatures in each state in the US to support this observance. On May 8, 1914, Woodrow Wilson was finally moved to make the second Sunday in May a national celebration for mothers. Unfortunately, Anna Jarvis eventually became discouraged to find that Mother's Day had been transformed from being the solemn commemoration she had envisioned into an overblown, commercial endeavor. Later in her life, she publicly decried companies such as Hallmark that had ruined the sacred event. In 1948, Anna died in a sanitarium, a blind, bitter, and lonely woman. Nevertheless, in a final gesture of kindness and reconciliation, Hallmark and the other commercial benefactors of Mother's Day paid her outstanding debts and funeral services.

More than 70 years later, Mother's Day remains a profitable commercial event. I find it a bit frightening to discover that Americans spend about $24 billion annually on cards, flowers, candies, and other gifts for our moms on this holiday. Mother's Day marks the busiest day for phone use, with each of us calling our mothers to express thanks for having the wisdom, grace, and patience for putting up with all our shenanigans. Clearly, celebrating our mothers with such pleasantries are all worthwhile endeavors. However, I think the greatest present we can give a woman bearing a child is the gift of being a mother beyond childbirth.

This is where Merck comes into play.

The World Health Organization (WHO) and United Nation's Children Fund (UNICEF) estimate that nearly 353,000 babies are born each day. While most mothers celebrate the birth of their newborn babies with pride, exuberance, and exhaustion, some moms are not so lucky. Each day, 830 women lose their lives during pregnancy, during childbirth, or in the postpartum period. Maternal mortality (MM), which is defined as any death while pregnant or 42 days following the termination of pregnancy, occurs predominantly in the developing world. In fact, the geographic and economic discrepancy in the maternal mortality ratio (MMR) is astounding; in 1990 the MMR was

239 maternal deaths/100 thousand live births in the developing world vs. 12 maternal deaths/100 thousand live births in the developed world. Most of the about 303,000 maternal deaths that occur each calendar year are preventable. Postpartum bleeding, pre-eclampsia, infection, and obstructed labor pose the greatest threat to maternal viability. However, other less common complications, such as blood clots, worsening of preexisting conditions, and unsafe abortion practices can also increase the risk for peripartum death. Although 99 percent of all deaths occur in the developing world, the track record in the developed world, even in the US, leaves much to be desired. While the MMR is improving in Africa (45 percent reduction), Latin America (50 percent reduction) and Southeast Asia (66 percent reduction), the MMR in the US is rising, placing our country at 46th on the current global list of countries with the lowest MMR. In 2015, the MMR in the US had climbed to 27 deaths/100 thousand live births, an increase from 14 thousand deaths/100 thousand in 1990. Sadly, the MMR in the US is nearly 3 to 4-fold higher in Blacks than in non-Blacks; poverty and insufficient health care are major forces driving this discrepancy. Even more concerning is the fact that more than 60 percent of these deaths in the US are preventable. Such statistics are staggering enough, but the cost of a lost mother in the physical and emotional impact on the wellbeing of her child, her partner, and her family unit, is equally devastating.

Fortunately, in 2012, Merck decided to do something to address MM. At that time, our company instituted the *Merck for Mothers* (MfM) global initiative. Since its inception, MfM has either initiated, supported, or funded over 50 different projects in 30 countries to reduce MM and improve the welfare of young women. MfM has trained over 144,000 healthcare workers in nearly 5,000 health facilities to provide quality care to expecting mothers. In turn, over seven million women have received improved access to affordable, quality healthcare. Along the way, over 100 corporate or social partners have joined the effort, thereby transforming MfM into one of the largest global efforts to tackle the MM problem.

It would be nearly impossible for me to do justice to all the awe-inspiring work that the MfM global team does. However, I can share with you some basic examples that highlight their 3 key mission goals: (1) **to develop innovative solutions to empower women** to seek the maternal care they deserve, whether by taking charge of their own health, making informed health choices, or demanding access to quality care; (2) **to strengthen capabilities of health providers to deliver high-quality care,** whether by improving training, escalating quality, or promoting novel, innovative products or digital tools; and (3) **to augment health systems for women,** whether by helping to advance quality standards, making life-saving products available, or generating evidence to support the cause. Here's a few brief examples to prove this point:

- Regarding *female empowerment*, MfM has helped renovate 25 shelters throughout Zambia to serve as a safe place for expecting mothers to stay while awaiting childbirth. The shelters are used by women who live far from health care facilities. Consequently, the rates of MM have fallen 41 percent in targeted regions in Zambia. Similarly, in Kenya, MfM created a social enterprise using a mobile phone-based service that educates Kenyan women about various family planning options and places where they can receive them.
- In relation to enhanced *health provider proficiency*, MfM launched MSD for Ugandan mothers (MUM), a service providing high-quality maternal health services via a network of private providers. MUM has enlisted the support of 140 private facilities and has trained 800 health workers in quality measures tied to maternal care and delivery. In doing so, MUM has helped expand access to quality healthcare to over 200,000 women in Uganda. In turn, the rates of MM have fallen 44 percent in targeted regions.
- To strengthen *existing health systems*, MfM has played an integral role in improving systems across the Southern Hemisphere. Take for instance the MfM program in Senegal. In this western African country, MfM has worked with the Bill and Melinda Gates Foundation, the local Senegalese government, and other organizations to scale up an innovative supply chain model to enhance the forecasting and delivery of contraceptives. These measures have reduced the rates of contraceptive stock-outs in Senegal from 80 percent to 2 percent.

These examples show the wide-ranging activities that MfM has engaged in across the globe. Their work also extends into the clinical development area. One of the biggest problems in sub-equatorial regions is the lack of access to essential medicines that prevent post-partum hemorrhage (PPH) following childbirth. Oxytocin, a peptide hormone, is the current standard of care, but this product requires a sustained cold chain at 2-8°C—a challenge for sub-Saharan

Africa and other developing regions. Together with the WHO and Ferring Pharmaceuticals, MfM supported the largest clinical trial ever conducted in PHH in to assess how the safety of a heat-stable oxytocin analogue, carbetocin, compared to oxytocin. Over 30 thousand pregnant women in ten countries participated in the CHAMPION Study between July 2015 and January 2018. Through MfM, Merck provided funding and scientific expertise to the trial design and conduct. The results confirmed that carbetocin was similar to oxytocin in preventing blood loss during pregnancy. The two treatment groups were also similar regarding many of the other primary and secondary efficacy outcomes and safety endpoints. The peer-reviewed results from the CHAMPION Study were recently published in the *New England Journal of Medicine*, and Ferring is now seeking WHO prequalification to ensure carbetocin's availability in those regions where refrigeration remains problematic. In short, the work MfM supports will help to save innumerable lives.

MfM initiatives have also been instrumental in helping curb MM in the US. MfM is working with the Center for Disease Control (CDC) Foundation to standardize data collection for maternal deaths throughout the US. These efforts will assess over 85 percent of all maternal deaths across 38 US states, thereby allowing preventive and therapeutic interventions to be targeted and fine-tuned for the regions most in need. In addition, in over 300 facilities across the US, MfM is helping its partners develop a set of standardized, evidence-based tools to prevent and treat the three leading killers of pregnant women in the US—embolism, pre-eclampsia, and PPH. Throughout rural areas of the US, MfM is also working to train and educate nurses and newly discharged mothers on the signs of potential life-threatening postpartum conditions. Through the Safer Childbirth Cities initiative, MfM provides grants to help cities with poor maternal health outcomes develop and implement creative, multi-sector solutions to save women's lives, improve maternal health, and narrow disparities across different races.

So, in closing, I'm thankful today for our company's leaders, whose foresight and vision led to the MfM initiative. I'm also grateful to the nearly 500 company ambassadors who provide their scientific, operational, and commercial expertise to MfM to address the epidemic of MM. The war on MM is a battle we can win. I'm proud of Merck's efforts in spearheading an initiative that saves the lives of so many mothers and will ultimately enhance the lives of thousands of new-born infants.

I'm obviously also thankful for my own mother, who reminds me through her own selfless actions that a parent's love is unconditional. Even though my mother lacks an education beyond sixth grade, she is one of the wisest humans I know. The life lessons she has taught me about kindness, devotion, and humility are priceless reminders I carry with me each day.

So, to all the mothers out there celebrating this upcoming Sunday, may your Mother's Day celebration be filled with joy, serenity, and love—just like Philadelphia's own Anna Marie Jarvis intended it to be.

20 A Dynamic Duo Deserving of Distinction *(May 16, 2019)*

For this week's *Thankful Thursday* segment, I'm planning to amplify the feminism-focused theme I started last week with my tribute to the *Merck for Mothers* initiative. However, unlike my last segment, this week's reflection concentrates on two extraordinary women, neither of which ever mothered any children. Yet both women gave birth to women in medicine. Today, I am deeply grateful to Elizabeth Blackwell and Florence Nightingale and their parallel pursuits that led to a monumental transformation in the field for medicine in the latter half of the nineteenth century. Through their daring and somewhat unorthodox efforts, this dynamic duo defied the discriminatory doctrine on doctoring, and, in turn, diversified modern medicine into what we know it is today.

This past Sunday, while the world celebrated Mother's Day, probably few people took notice of the 199th birthday of Florence Nightingale. Born into a wealthy English family on May 12, 1820, Florence Nightingale became the founder of modern nursing. Within a year, another incredible woman, Elizabeth Blackwell, would also be born into an English family, in the town of Bristol. Elizabeth Blackwell became the first woman to receive a medical degree in the United States and the first to be recognized within the British Medical Register of the General Medical Council. Along the way, she promoted the education of women as physicians and pioneered the first medical schools dedicated solely to women in both the United States and England. During their lifetimes, these two English women would share many features. Both were born to parents who ardently advocated for gender equality in their children's scholarly pursuits. Both would also engage in social reform. In addition to their long-held views supporting woman's rights, the two also held fervent abolitionist views, advocated for the cessation of child labour, and campaigned for sanitary living conditions for all classes of society, not just for those who could afford it. Neither woman would marry. As Elizabeth Blackwell so poignantly put it, "The fact is that I cannot find my other half, but only about a sixth, which will not do."[22] Both suffered infectious ailments that physically crippled them but failed to hinder their ambitions. Both would live prosperous lives to the age of 90, and they died in close proximity to one another in England. Most importantly, Elizabeth Blackwell and Florence Nightingale became life-long companions and trusted confidantes. Although their views contrasted on several occasions, their divergent perspectives championed the simultaneous birth of two novel disciplines: nursing and women as physicians.

Let's get to know these two luminaries a bit more, starting with Dr. Elizabeth Blackwell.

Born into a family of nine children, Elizabeth Blackwell emigrated with her parents and siblings to the United States when she was 11 years old. After a few years in New York City, her family settled in Cincinnati. Their father, Samuel, educated all his children in the finer arts of language, science, mathematics, and music. However, tragedy struck the Blackwell family when Samuel died in 1838, at a time when Elizabeth was just 17. To support the family, Elizabeth and her sisters formed a school in Ohio for young ladies. In due time, Elizabeth set off on her own to serve as a schoolteacher, first in Henderson, Kentucky, and then in Asheville, North Carolina. Horrified by the wretched school conditions and the despairing effect of slavery on Southern society, she grew discontent with the life of a schoolteacher. Two events sparked a career change. First, in 1844, she visited a dying friend who was suffering from what was most likely uterine cancer; unfortunately, her friend was in an advanced stage of the disease, having been too embarrassed to visit a male physician until it was too late. On her death bed, she told Elizabeth that she was cared for by a

---

22 From *Pioneer Work in Opening the Medical Profession to Women* by Elizabeth Blackwell: London: J. M. Dent & Sons, 1914.

rough, unfeeling man. She told Elizabeth that had a lady doctor been available, she might have pursued earlier treatment and been spared the embarrassment of her fatal predicament. Second, in 1845, while in Asheville, Elizabeth lodged with a physician and local reverend who took her under his wing. He gladly shared his medical library with the erudite Elizabeth in exchange for piano and other music lessons for the students in his North Carolinian school.

Elizabeth grew to love medicine and aspired to become a physician. She moved to Philadelphia in 1847 to pursue a medical degree. She applied to all 29 US medical schools at the time, including 12 country schools. Sadly, 28 schools rejected her, including Philadelphia's Jefferson Medical College, which informed her that they would only consider her application if she were willing to attend disguised as a man. Fortunately, one medical school, the Geneva Medical School, on what is now the campus of Hobart College in upstate New York, agreed to her admission. Over the next two years, Elizabeth completed her medical studies and practiced at Philadelphia's Blockley Almshouse, despite the refusal of some professors to permit her attendance at medical demonstrations. In 1849, at the age of 29, Elizabeth graduated as the valedictorian of her medical school class. As Geneva's dean, Dr. Charles Lee, conferred the medical degree upon her, he graciously bowed to Dr. Blackwell in recognition of her academic perseverance. Soon after, Elizabeth set off to Europe to pursue training as a surgeon.

In the spring of 1850, she met a young woman named Florence Nightingale at her home, *Embley Park*, in Hampshire, England. At this point, Florence was 30 years old. Like Elizabeth, she was a bright, ambitious individual who was well versed in mathematics, science, and the language arts. Despite her mother's protestations and the anti-feminist social code of Victorian England, her father encouraged her pursuit of her one true love, the science of nursing. As an affluent family, the Nightingales had travelled extensively to Italy, Greece, and Egypt, where Florence studied ancient medicine. As a woman's career in nursing was taboo in Britain, Florence received four months of medical training in Germany, a country which was socially less restrictive at the time and was making notable advances in medicinal chemistry, hygiene, and other sanitary practices. When Florence and Elizabeth met at her family's estate, Florence revealed her vision of caring for the ill, invalid, and poor, even joking of transforming the family's austere drawing room at *Embley Park* into a functioning hospital ward. Elizabeth departed after a few weeks' stay with her new-found friend to study obstetrics in Paris.

A few years later, it would be Florence Nightingale's turn to have a moment in the sun. In 1853, the Crimean War had erupted over the proprietary rights to the Holy Land. The conflict pitted the Russian Empire against the confederacy of Britain, France, and the Ottoman Empire. The harsh, brutal conditions on the war front in Scutari, near Istanbul, had caused rampant infection, including typhoid, typhus, and cholera. These epidemics afflicting the British troops were exacerbated by crowded infirmaries, an indifference to hygiene, and substandard sanitation practices. At the bidding of Britain's Secretary of War, who was a family friend of the Nightingales, Florence trained 38 volunteer nurses and 15 Catholic nuns and then made the treacherous trek over 300 miles to the British camp in Scutari. In due time, the team cared for the ill and ameliorated the deplorable conditions by instituting basic nursing care, improved sanitation, and good hygiene practices, such as handwashing. Mortality rates plummeted from 42 percent to 2 percent. Florence often toiled late into the night, carrying a small lamp on solitary rounds, during which she ministered to the infirm. *The London Times* recounted tales of the Lady of the Lamp, portraying Florence as a selfless, compassionate hero of the brutal conflict. Unfortunately, during her stay, she contracted brucellosis, and this bacterial infection would plague her with chronic fevers and musculoskeletal pains for the remainder of her life. Undeterred, she continued her quest to improve health conditions in Britain. Upon her return from the military conflict, she wrote *Notes on Nursing: What It Is and What It is Not,* a keystone publication on the proper self-education of nurses at home. With the assistance of monies raised by the public, called the Nightingale Fund, she founded the first nursing school in England, which is now part of Kings College London.

Florence Nightingale envisioned the ideal superintendent for her new nursing school to be Elizabeth Blackwell. While in Paris, Elizabeth had mastered obstetric surgery, but a tragic accident prohibited her pursuit of this vocation. While caring for a neonate suffering from what was likely gonococcal ophthalmia, Elizabeth inadvertently sprayed contaminated water in her own eye and contracted the infection. Sadly, the infection persisted and eventually required the surgical extraction of her eye. Her career as a surgeon was over. After this unfortunate turn of events, Florence pursued Elizabeth to become the administrative superintendent of her nursing school. However, Elizabeth balked at the proposition because Florence's curriculum failed to permit graduating nurses to complete their educational studies as physicians. Florence viewed this idea of transforming a nurse into a physician as training of a mischievous nature, informing Elizabeth that their philosophical differences could not be reconciled. She articulated the difference in their goals: "You to educate a few highly cultivated [women] – I to diffuse as much knowledge as possible."[23]

In 1859, Dr. Blackwell decided to return to the United States to pursue her vision of caring for patients and forming a medical school dedicated to women. Prior to her departure, she secured one important victory: being named the first female physician in Britain's Medical Register of the General Medical Council. Upon her arrival in the US, Elizabeth opened a private practice in NYC, but the patients never materialized due to the then-prevalent social bias of being cared for by a female physician. So Elizabeth became a public orator, espousing best practices to expectant mothers. She gradually gained visibility in the city. In time, she saved enough money to open an infirmary for impoverished women. She joined forces with her sister Emily, who had recently graduated as a physician from Western Reserve University in Cleveland (now Case Western). Their New York Infirmary for Indigent Women and Children grew in stature and fame, with Elizabeth as the director and Emily as the surgeon. Both did their part to support the Civil War effort. Although the social milieu at the time forbade Elizabeth from serving as a physician during the war, she helped the war effort by enlisting and training volunteer women to serve as battlefield nurses under the leadership of Dorothea Dix.

By 1868, the Blackwell sisters had raised enough funds to install a medical school at their Infirmary, entitled the Women's Medical College of the New York Infirmary. The school, which was the first such institution in the United States, included another first: a four-year medical program. A four-year training curriculum is now the norm of most US medical schools.

---

23 "The Art of Medicine" by Julia Boyd, published in *Lancet*, Volume 373, 2009, page 1516.

Elizabeth returned to London in 1869 and rekindled her friendship with Florence. By that time, Florence Nightingale, who had cemented her legacy as the founder of modern nursing, had begun to tackle sanitation reform. Poor sewer drainage, contaminated water supply, and inadequate ventilation were rampant in Victorian England and many of its colonies. With attention to detail and her knowledge of mathematics, Florence Nightingale chronicled these social problems and campaigned for change. She collected and compiled data and then depict the results using visually-appealing diagrams. She helped pioneer the use of statistical graphics, such as pie charts and histograms, to illustrate poor conditions in hospitals, military barracks, and workhouses throughout England and India. In the 1870s, her advances in public health statistics earned her positions as the first woman in the Royal Statistical Society and as an honorary member of the American Statistical Association. Elizabeth Blackwell eventually partnered with Florence Nightingale and Dr. Elizabeth Garrett Anderson, who was the first practicing female physician in England. Together, they inaugurated the first medical school for women in England. The board of the new London School of Medicine for Women appointed Elizabeth Blackwell as its first Chair of Hygiene. Hundreds of women went on to become nurses and physicians on both sides of the Atlantic in the late nineteenth century. All the while, both Elizabeth and Florence wrote books and gave oral presentations promoting their common social missions—improved sanitation, preventive medicine, elimination of child labour practices, and women's rights.

In early 1910, both visionaries would fall ill. Elizabeth Blackwell died after suffering a fall and subsequent stroke in Sussex, England, in May 1910. A few months later, Florence Nightingale succumbed to brucellosis. She died in London, under the care and attention of two physicians. Female physicians, of course.

Medicine shouldn't be influenced by gender, but it is a bit sobering to realize that it wasn't too long ago that women had little role in this profession. So today, I am thankful for the vision, missionary spirit, and tenacity that these two incredible pioneers, Elizabeth Blackwell and Florence Nightingale, brought to modern medicine. Their disparate approaches were somewhat foreign to one another at the time. Yet together this dynamic duo set forward multiple pathways for women to become a veritable force in medicine. At the turn of the twentieth century, medical schools for women began to close as major universities such as Colombia, Harvard, and Cornell began accepting women to their medical schools. Many colleges and universities would also open nursing schools, and now over 3,000 such schools are in existence in the US. Today, nursing in the United States remains a female-dominated profession, with over 90 percent of all registered nurses being women. As for medical doctors in the US, approximately 33 percent of practicing physicians are women, but the numbers are rapidly rising. In fact, more women (50.7 percent) than men (49.3 percent) were newly enrolled in US medical schools in 2017. Incidentally, here at Merck, within the ID/Vaccines Therapeutic Area to which I help provide oversight, approximately 55 percent of the clinical director staff are women and approximately 60 percent of the development team leaders are women. Similarly, in Merck's clinical trial operations and statistical organizations, women fill many of the roles that help to propel forward our clinical development programs.

So we all owe a debt of gratitude to folks like Elizabeth Blackwell and Florence Nightingale. This dynamic duo played an instrumental role in transforming the collective thinking of women in medicine. Outside of my work environment, I do not need to look too far from my own home to appreciate how things have also changed for the better. My mother-in-law, Gwynneth, is now retired after a successful career as an intensive care unit nurse at the Columbia-Presbyterian Medical Center in New York City. Her oldest daughter, my partner, Daisy, became a successful physician who graduated from the College of Physicians and Surgeons (now, the Columbia University Vagelos College of Physicians and Surgeons, thanks to the generous donations of Merck's former CEO). Interestingly, both my mother-in-law and my wife trained a stone's throw away from where Dr. Blackwell set up her New York Infirmary over 160 years ago. Needless to say, I have immense love and genuine gratitude for both Gwynneth and Daisy—my own dynamic duo of distinction.

If you are interested in learning more, I point you to two books:

1. Boyd J., *The Excellent Doctor Blackwell: The Life of the First Female Physician*, Published by Sutton Publishing in 2006.

2. Bostridge M. *Florence Nightingale: The Making of an Icon*, Published by Viking in 2008.

21 Kudos for Those Kindling Kindness *(May 23, 2019)*

For this week's *Thankful Thursday* segment, I wish to express my gratitude to those colleagues who took time to show me that one behavior that supersedes all others—kindness. In my career, I've had the opportunity to interact with many individuals who have taught me that generosity is not only the lynchpin that strengthens all workplace relationships but also a quintessential quality of leadership. I hope to inspire each of you to display unselfish acts of goodwill in your daily interactions.

Defining the term *kindness* is not an easy task. If you were to consult a dictionary, it would probably define the word as a behavior that is marked by ethical tenets, with an outward focus and concern for others. Throughout history, many great philosophers, scientists, and authors have grappled with the definition. Aristotle, who was the third in the line of great Greek philosophers and a learned pupil of Plato, defines kindness as "helpfulness towards someone in need, not in return for anything, nor for the advantage of the helper himself but for that of the person helped."[24] Perhaps this is why Aristotle is so loved even to this day, but he's no Socrates. The English physicist Isaac Newton referred to kindness by calling out what we need to do more: "Men build too many walls and not enough bridges."[25] Well, that's

---

24 From Book II of *Rhetoric*, by Aristotle in 4th Century BC

25 Although this quotation has been widely attributed to Isaac Newton, the text has not been found in any of his writings. The quote was made famous by the Dominican priest Dominique Pire in his Nobel Lecture in

clearly an interesting perspective in these modern days. Finally, the great American novelist Mark Twain may have put it best: "Kindness is the language the deaf can hear and the blind can see."[26] Mark Twain was known to assist those less fortunate than himself—including those who were blind and deaf.

Throughout history, we've witnessed great men and women exhibiting kindness in times of need. A case in point is Oskar Schindler, the German Catholic factory owner who protected over 1,200 Jewish workers during the Nazi Holocaust by falsifying records, bribing SS officers, and even physically housing his targeted Jewish workers within the walls of his fortified factory. One can also find acts of kindness in individuals like Mother Theresa, who dedicated her life to caring for the impoverished in India, or Pope John Paul II, who forgave Mehmet Ali Agca, the man who attempted to assassinate him in 1981. More recently, we've seen accounts of generosity in places like Japan, where over 200 elderly engineers volunteered to be the first responders to the humanitarian crisis in the Fukushima nuclear power plant in 2011. Here in the US, the recently-retired (it saddens me immensely to write this!) Philadelphia Eagle, Chris Long, is another example of someone who exhibited kindness in all he did. He contributed a significant portion of one year's salary to endow scholarships for the victims in his hometown of Charlottesville, as well as the entirety of his next year's salary to support underprivileged youth in the three cities in which he played professional football—St. Louis, Boston, and Philadelphia. He spearheaded an international program, *Waterboys,* which provides clean, potable water in parts of East Africa. No wonder he's the latest recipient of the NFL's most coveted prize, the Walter Payton Man of the Year Award. Kindness was also recently on display in France: Did any of you happen to see the Malian immigrant who risked his own life a year ago to climb four balconies up the side of a Parisian apartment complex to rescue a four-year old French boy dangling from the edge? If you haven't seen this veritable Spiderman in action, I'd suggest you check it out on the

---

December 1958, but the Nobel Peace Prize winner referred to Newton by only the last name. He might actually have been paraphrasing another Newton, the Baptist minister and freemason Joseph Ford Newton, who had once written that men are inhabited by fear "...erecting walls around themselves instead of building bridges into the lives of others..."

26 Attributed to Mark Twain by Walter Winchell in 1942. See https://quoteinvestigator.com/2013/10/26/kindness-see/.

Internet. Altogether, these examples paint an accurate account of individuals exhibiting kindness by making sacrifices to help others in need.

Some would argue that the greatest of human qualities are best displayed through art. I've wondered whether there was a movie, a play, or a song that I could reference that displays the true essence of kindness. I considered referencing the 2011 movie *Pay It Forward,* which tells a fictional account of how a good deed paid forward unleashes a virtuous cycle of positive events. However, the fictitious nature of the events and the recent, unflattering circumstances of the movie's lead actor made me nix that idea. I wondered if I could reference the last few scenes in *Hamilton,* as they portray an incredible act of forgiveness and love in our American history. But then I realized if I did so, I might ruin the musical for all those who've yet to see what I believe is a spectacular form of art in motion. In the end, I decided a song would be the best way to go. Natalie Merchant ("Kind and Generous"), Selena Gomez ("Kill Them with Kindness"), and Don Henley ("Heart of the Matter") have all crafted masterful songs that speak to the power of gratitude, civility, and forgiveness.

But, today belongs to the singer Jewel. In her song "Hands," Jewel eloquently speaks to the power of positivity, reminding us that "light does the darkness most fear." She lyricizes about helping those in need when they themselves cannot speak on their own behalf: "We'll fight, not out of spite, for someone must stand up for what's right. Cause when there's a man who has no voice, there ours shall go singing." But it is the one lyric in the middle of the song that she aptly chose to repeat for artistic effect that sums it all: "In the end, only kindness matters."

Today, I'd like to pause and salute Jewel for all she's taught me about the power of kindness. It seems appropriate for me to do so on this specific day, since Jewel celebrates her 45th birthday today. In her life, Jewel has demonstrated resilience in the face of enduring hardship, and yet she's also been the recipient of many generous favors from a host of individuals. Her song "Hands" pays tribute to those who helped her reach the pinnacle of success.

Let's get to know this wonderful artist a bit more.

Born in Utah to Mormon parents, Jewel Kilcher and her family moved to Homer, Alaska, where she was essentially raised off the grid. She's the daughter of Atz Kilcher, whose life has been chronicled in

"Alaska: The Last Frontiers," a reality wilderness show on the Discovery Channel. I proudly admit that I've seen many episodes of this show, as I'm always fascinated to see self-sufficiency and perseverance in the face of little to no modern technology. Jewel's family recognized that she was gifted with a pleasing soprano voice. In her preteen years, Jewel routinely played in a father-daughter duet in hotel bars throughout Anchorage. The community recognized her talents, and when she was 15, she won entry to Interlochen Center for the Arts in Michigan. Lacking the means to pay the tuition, although she had a partial scholarship, Jewel received the first of many acts of kindness—the entire Homer community donated items for auction and collected donations to cover her remaining tuition, as well as room and board. While at school, Jewel received training in operatic singing, and she learned to play the guitar. Following graduation, she moved to San Diego, where she unfortunately found herself homeless, living in her car while working as a barista and playing her songs in coffeehouses. One Thursday evening, while singing in a local café, a second act of kindness was bestowed on Jewel—she was recognized by John Hogan, the lead singer of the band Rust. He convinced a friend at Atlantic Records to give Jewel a demo audition. Once music executives heard Jewel sing, they offered her the opportunity to sign on under their label. By that time, she was becoming recognized as a musical phenomenon. This is when the third act of kindness was afforded Jewel—musician greats Bob Dylan and Neil Young befriended her and served as mentors. As Jewel lacked a band to perform with, Neil Young arranged for her to record her first album, *Pieces of You*, in a studio on his ranch, supported by his own backing band, The Stray Gators. The album became an instant success.

Since her initial release nearly 25 years ago, Jewel has continued to refine her singing. Heeding the advice of Bob Dylan, she produced eclectic albums with disparate themes: rock, country, dance, and pop. With 12 albums now under her belt, Jewel has grown both as a musician and a poet. All the while, Jewel never forgot the power of giving back. She founded a non-profit organization, Higher Ground for Humanity, which is focused on education, sustainable improvements, and building alliances around the world. The organization was one of the first entities to support the Global Youth Action Network, which has since grown into one of the largest youth movements supported by the United Nations. She leads a charitable organization called Project Clean Water, which has helped to bring potable water and other sanitation measures to 15 developing countries. Chris Long would be thrilled! She recently started a new venture, The Never Broken Foundation, which makes tools for mindfulness and emotional intelligence freely available via the internet. In short, Jewel has taken the good fortunes proffered to her and she is paying it forward to those in need.

We can all probably recount acts of kindness that others have bestowed upon us in our careers or personal lives. It's somewhat cathartic for me to share a few such examples in my career to help dispel that long-held myth that no good deed goes unpunished. Specifically, I share three instances, one each during my time in medical school, my time in residency/fellowship training, and my early Merck career that exemplify the one theme that Jewel so beautifully articulated—in the end, only kindness matters.

First, let's start with medical school. In 1993 when I was a third-year medical student at the Emory University School of Medicine, I was extremely apprehensive about starting my rotational rounds on the wards. The towering walls of Grady Memorial Hospital was enough to make any medical student tremble in his shoes. My first rotation in downtown Atlanta was in Obstetrics and Gynecology (OB/GYN). I was paired with a medical school colleague, David Cooperberg, who is now a pediatrician in Philadelphia. During the first week of the rotation, we were assigned to the Gynecological Surgery team, where we assisted operations by holding retractors for endless hours in a drab operating room. One day, prior to surgical gowning, we were confronted by the then-former Chair of Grady's OB/GYN Department. Knowing he was in the presence of several intimidated novices, you might guess that he would greet us, get to know us, and welcome us to the world of OB/GYN. Unfortunately, he took an opposing tact. Taking an intimidating tone, the doctor pounded us ruthlessly with obstetrical questions. After we did our best to answer the questions, he turned his attention to me. "Let me ask you a question: I see you want to become a doctor, but it is evident to me that you bite your nails. Don't you think this is a vile, unsanitary act unbefitting of a physician?" I sat dumbfounded, unable to speak. Then, the true act of kindness revealed itself. My colleague David turned to him and quipped: "Let me ask you a question, Dr. X. It appears odd that you mistreat students in such an esteemed institution of higher learning. Is it really befitting of a physician to be so rude to others?" The physician stopped short, downplayed his bullying behaviour as nothing more than a joke, and left the room. I never encountered the former Chair again. I tell you this story because it shows that sometimes kindness comes from a courageous individual willing to stick out his/her own neck to defend another person's honor and dignity. Sometimes, as Jewel quipped, "someone must stand up for what's right 'cause when there's a man who has no voice, there ours shall go singing."

Second, let's travel forward five years to my third year of my medical residency. After medical school, I headed north to train in Internal Medicine at Massachusetts General Hospital (MGH) in Boston. By my third and last residency year in 1997, I was exhausted, but, nonetheless, I had made up my mind to pursue an Infectious Diseases fellowship. One of the final activities prior to completing my Internal Medicine residency was to give a mandatory lunchtime lecture to all the residents. I chose the topic "Tick Diseases in the Bay State." I reached out to the former Chair of Infectious Diseases at MGH, Dr. Morton Swartz, to discuss my upcoming presentation. For those of you who've never had the pleasure to meet this genteel physician, I think the only true way I can describe Dr. Swartz is as the kindest, smartest, and most unpretentious physician I have ever met. In possession of an encyclopedic memory, Dr. Swartz knew every detail about every topic, but his greatest attribute was his sincere, heartfelt combination of kindness and humility. Dr. Swartz informed me that he would not only review my presentation but also happily attend my lecture to provide moral support. Dr. Swartz also provided me with invaluable input that enhanced my presentation by sharing a few of his own personal slides to support my endeavor. The presentation came and went without incident. Later that year, I began my ID fellowship at the Combined Partners Program at MGH and Brigham's Women Hospital (BWH). In the first 12 months, I was somewhat dumbfounded by the sheer number of phone calls I received from local physicians regarding tick diseases, and fortunately my lecture was still fresh enough in my mind to answer those queries. What I did not know was that Dr. Swartz, in all his prominence and benevolence, was the individual actually receiving these calls. Instead of answering them, and he clearly knew the answers, he would selflessly triage them to me, often calling me the "true local expert in tick diseases in Massachusetts." This was called to my attention by a friend, who was a physician-in-training across town. One evening, my friend called me laughing and said: "Since when did you become the all-knowing expert of tick diseases in Massachusetts?" When I asked what he was referring to, he told me how his attending physician was excited to learn that he had just discussed a case with the renowned expert, Dr. Nicholas Kartsonis. The attending physician went on to say that he got the name of this expert from Dr. Morton Swartz, so he knew it had to be true, coming from such an esteemed, reliable source. I sheepishly shared the story with Dr. Swartz later that week at a weekly intercity conference, and he responded that it was time for him to "hand over the reins to the next generation of leaders." Dr. Swartz's kindness as a mentor is something I'll never forget. In fact, when I decided to join Merck a few years later, Dr. Swartz was the most vocal advocate within the department who encouraged me to do so. Sadly, Dr. Swartz passed away a few years back. Prior to his death, I did have the opportunity to see him in Boston at an MGH event, where I personally thanked him for his years of support.

Finally, let me share a story from my first year at Merck in 2000. I was encouraged by my manager, Carole Sable, to present the latest caspofungin data at Merck's Closed Research Update at the International Conference on Antimicrobial Agents and Chemotherapy, an event attended by nearly 300 experts in the field of mycology. These physicians were attending because many were intrigued to learn about the echinocandins, the newest class of antifungals. Intimidated, anxious, and apprehensive, I spent a week familiarizing myself with the available data for Merck's first-in-class echinocandin, caspofungin. However, when the big day came, I totally flopped. I spoke way too fast and failed to answer the audience questions accurately. Worse, my shaking hands were on full display, complicating any attempt to highlight key data on the slides with the laser pointer. As one of the key scientific leaders later told me at the dinner table, "The spastic red laser on the slides looked like flies circulating over human [excrement]." Instead of piling on, my manager, Carole, took me aside that evening, shared her own prior less-than-stellar experiences in public speaking, and informed me of her willingness to mentor me to become a more poised, refined speaker. Prior to my next talk, she let me deliver a dry run to her as a single-person audience and offered priceless pointers. She even advocated for my attendance at a Merck-supported course, "Powerful Presentations." The next year, I had the opportunity to watch Carole present at several painful FDA Advisory Committee prep sessions for caspofungin, where I learned even more from her graceful approach. In due time, my comfort level rose and my skills in delivering a presentation improved. When my time came to answer complex questions at a contentious FDA Advisory Committee meeting a few years back, I channeled my inner Carole and did my best to stay calm and carry on. To this day, I feel enormous gratitude to Carole for her generosity and warmth. She was a kind leader who taught me that shining a light does indeed cause the darkness most fear.

OK, now I hope you appreciated the one common theme besides kindness in these three stories. If you're not too sure, re-familiarize yourself with the title of Jewel's song about kindness.

All too often, leaders believe the way to succeed and climb the professional ladder is to follow a Darwinist "survival of the fittest" mantra. But, the truth be told that a "me first" approach that emphasizes abruptness, selfishness, and indifference to others within the organization is nothing more than a recipe for disaster. Indeed, I fully acknowledge that successful leaders need intelligence, cognitive skills, and wisdom garnered from their prior experiences to do their jobs effectively. However, to truly succeed, leaders need to become agents of emotional intelligence. I recently read *Primal Leadership: Unleashing the Power of Emotional Intelligence*. In this book, the authors say that among the 18 leadership competencies of emotionally-intelligent leaders are empathy, service to the organization and its people, inspiration, self-control, development of others, teamwork and collaboration, optimism, and transparency. When one thinks about kindness in the workplace, it starts with being genuinely considerate to your colleagues. Whenever someone is being empathetic, service-oriented, inspirational, collaborative, optimistic, or simply transparent, that individual is exhibiting the core elements of kindness, respect, and humility. In short, the best and most emotionally intelligent leaders succeed because they put others first. Sage individuals like Aristotle, Newton, and Twain were correct in their declarations that it all starts with kindness.

Not only do these competencies help your colleagues and the whole organization, but they also have a lasting personal effect on you. Exhibiting kindness has a positive impact on one's own physical and emotional wellbeing, a phenomenon known as a helper's high. Research has shown that individuals who exhibit kindness release substances that have positive effects on themselves. Performing kind acts—whether at work, at home, or in your community—can lead to the following: (1) the hormonal production of oxytocin, which aids in releasing nitrous oxide, an agent that lowers blood pressure and provides cardio-protection; (2) the release of serotonin, a neurotransmitter that increases one's calmness and lowers depressive tendencies; and (3) an increase in neuropeptides, including endorphins, which are the natural painkillers that are often achieved from a runner's high. Gentle, considerate, and warm tendencies also ameliorate one's own heightened state of anxiety and stress by reducing cortisol synthesis. Altruistic behaviors, even in the work setting, have been associated with long-lasting happiness, fewer musculoskeletal pains, and a greater life expectancy.

My advice to all of you is to find time to perform acts of kindness at work. Here's seven simple, kind tasks you can do in your daily interactions:

1. When in the hallway, take the moment to say hello or smile to a passerby, even if he/she is an absolute stranger. Your random act of kindness might be the stimulus that person needs to come up with an innovative idea, discover the solution to a work-related problem, or garner the strength to address a personnel conundrum.
2. Whenever you are in a meeting, take the time to listen attentively to your colleagues' viewpoints. Irrespective of whether you agree or disagree with the perspective at hand, thank the person for sharing his/her viewpoint.
3. Send a thank you email to someone who has gone above and beyond the call of duty. Everyone appreciates a personal note from a colleague.
4. Better yet, use Merck's electronic reward and recognition system to send along your appreciation, as it allows your gratitude to be amplified throughout the entire company. The system is so easy that I bet it took just as long for me to write these few sentences in this paragraph as it would for you to open the system and craft a short note of thanks.
5. For those of you who lead teams, take the time to personally coach a less experienced team member.
6. For those senior leaders who provide oversight to large groups, pay it forward by serving as a mentor to a young, aspiring leader. We'll address the topic of mentorship in a future *Thankful Thursday* segment.

7. When asked by colleagues to share feedback, seize on the opportunity to do so in a thoughtful, professional, and accurate manner. In fact, most individuals crave feedback so they themselves can continuously improve. Nobody wants to wallow in mediocrity, so view feedback as a gift. We all want to learn from our mistakes and grow in our roles. We also want others to speak to us in a forthright way. Frank communication is healthy and it ultimately allows for mutual respect and admiration.

I guess what I'm saying can be summed up best by the following: An attitude of gratitude is easy and probably just as contagious as a highly infectious disease—like measles. OK, I realize that was a really tacky joke, but I'm really trying to emphasize a crucial point here.

Listen, I am fully aware of how busy we all are. We often do not have the time to shoot the breeze at the water cooler or lollygag in the cafeteria. Nevertheless, I promise you that the good deeds you take the time to perform will reap rewards several-fold for both you and the recipient.

So today I'm thankful for all those who took the time to offer me their kindness, generosity, and virtuous regard. Their generous approach has afforded me the ability to grow in my role and to recognize what is truly important. After nearly two decades working at Merck, I've come to realize that the legacy I want to be remembered for is as someone who was there to lend a helping hand to a colleague in need. Although we are all employed by Merck to develop, manufacture, and commercialize drugs, vaccines, and biologics for the betterment of humankind, our real purpose is to leave this awesome company in a better state than when we found it. Our legacy is the people we leave behind to run Merck when we are gone. Don't you want the person that succeeds you to be an individual who is kind, trustworthy, and empathetic?

If you remember nothing else from this blog, just look at your hands and remember these six simple words from the song with the same title: "In the end, only kindness matters."

P.S. If you are interested in learning more about the power of emotional intelligence, I point you to the Book Club read: *Primal Leadership: Unleashing the Power of Emotional Intelligence* by Daniel Goleman, Richard Boyatzis, and Annie McKee. Harvard Business Review Press, 2013.

22 Exalting Those Explorers Who Endeavor to End an Evil Epidemic *(May 30, 2019)*

For this week's *Thankful Thursday* segment, I'd like to praise those scientists who have toiled over the last 35 years to fight the most devastating epidemic we've witnessed in our lifetime. The unrelenting commitment against human immunodeficiency virus (HIV), the virus responsible for the acquired immunodeficiency syndrome (AIDS), is a testimony of the ingenuity and resiliency of humankind. I believe that the contributions that scientists at Merck, other pharmaceutical companies, and academic and public institutions have made to HIV discovery over the last three decades have not only changed the world but have set us on the path that will lead one day to a cure for this societal scourge.

In the past, I've shared stories about Thomas Edison, the Wizard of Menlo Park. Edison, like many of his predecessors, such as Leonardo Da Vinci, Johannes Gutenberg, and Benjamin Franklin, shared one common belief: Invention does not come easy, but in a slow, laborious, and sometimes mundane process of trial and error. Although I've talked about the power or serendipity in my prior chapters, most discoveries do not come by chance. Rather, it's a commitment to diligence, an openness to experimentation, and the courage to fail that allow the greatest inventors, engineers, and scientists to gain enlightenment. It's not by accident that Edison famously quipped: "Genius is one percent inspiration, ninety nine percent perspiration."[27] Every discovery has a defined starting point. From the onset of your journey, you need to possess the fortitude and willingness to course-correct as the situation dictates, because the path you anticipate will likely require some modification. Along the way, the knowledge gleaned from your explorations will hopefully reap fascinating advances and uncover untrodden inroads. It might not be a path you first envisioned travelling. Nevertheless, you should never shy away from continuing your pursuit down that unchartered path, for it might ultimately lead you to your desired destination.

Let's use the exploration of the American West as a case in point. Two of the most renowned explorations of this nation's rugged terrain began years ago this week.

Hernando de Soto, the great Spanish explorer, landed in Florida near Tampa Bay on this day 480 years ago. As one of Spain's great conquistadors, de Soto was no novice to exploration. In years leading up to his arrival in North America, he played an integral role in the expeditions leading to the discovery of the Yucatan Peninsula, Nicaragua, and Peru, ultimately returning to Spain in 1536 with spoils from his conquest of the Inca Empire. However, he is most famous in our textbooks for the odyssey that led him across most of what is now the southeastern portion of the United States. When de Soto landed in Florida in 1539, his intent was to complete a 4-year pillage-and-plunder trek of the North American region in search of gold for the Spanish Empire. With over 600 men, 220 horses, 200 pigs, and a slew of bloodhounds, he trailblazed a path that would take him up through modern-day Georgia, South Carolina, and North Carolina, and then southwest to Tennessee, Alabama, and Mississippi. Nearly two years later, in May 1541, he would become the first European to navigate the Mississippi River. Unfortunately, his trail was one filled with much misery, anguish, and sorrow—and no gold. De Soto terrorized the Native Americans with his hostile, abrasive manner, and, to make matters worse, spread the diseases measles, smallpox, and chicken pox to these non-immune populations. In a somewhat fitting retribution, the harsh winter of 1541 would strike back and decimate

---

27 Statement made in a press conference in1929, quoted in *Uncommon Friends: Life with Thomas Edison, Henry Ford, Harvey Firestone, Alexis Carrel & Charles Lindbergh* (1987) by James D. Newton, p. 24.

his troop. De Soto died the next spring of fever and was buried along the western bank of the Mississippi river. By the time the expedition ended in late 1543, his outfit had only 300 men surviving. Although the European world would gain knowledge of the geography and biology of the southern United States from the recorded chronicles of his adventures, de Soto left behind a mistrust of Europeans, a litany of infectious diseases, and a slew of swine (the ancestral lineage of the feral razorback hogs that still ransack the South today). De Soto's expedition was not a success, but his ill-fated trek taught the early English, French, and Spanish settlers of colonial America one important lesson: If you opt to explore the West, you had better be prepared. And, oh, by the way, it might help to take a kinder, gentler approach to the native populations.

More than a quarter of a millennium later, a more ceremonious voyage across the remainder of the United States would begin in late May 1804 at the banks of the Mississippi River, essentially where de Soto had left off. After successfully negotiating the most famous fleecing in real estate history, the third United States President, Thomas Jefferson, arranged an expedition of these newfound territories with two intents in mind: (1) to survey a practical, all-water passage across the western part of the North American continent; and (2) to study the geography, nature, and local inhabitants of this unexplored land.

However, unlike de Soto, Jefferson planned ahead by commissioning a Corps of Discovery led by Army Captain Meriwether Lewis and his second-in-command, William Clark, a renowned frontiersman and infantry lieutenant. Jefferson sent Lewis to Philadelphia to study under Dr. Benjamin Rush and the astronomer Andrew Ellicott so he could have some comprehension of contemporary medical practices and navigational skills. He spent time at Jefferson's Monticello home in Charlottesville, where he read from the President's large collection of maps and books, which Jefferson had assembled in his library from his worldwide travels. Then, in late May 1804, Lewis and Clark embarked with 29 others, mostly US Army personnel, on an 8,000-mile trek, starting from the banks of the Mississippi River near St. Louis. Using mostly river passages, they traveled Northwest through what is now Missouri, Nebraska, and Iowa before reaching the Great Plains. As they encountered native Americans, they often negotiated peaceful passage through these occupied territories using their skills of negotiation, offering silver medals and an occasional bottle or two of whiskey. They settled in modern day North Dakota for the first winter, where they met members of the Shoestone tribe, including a young woman, named Sacagawea, who would serve as a trusted translator and guide. In Spring of 1805, they continued via the Yellowstone and Marias Rivers through the Yellowstone region into Montana, crossed the Continental Divide at Lehmi Pass near Idaho, and traversed down a number of rivers before reaching the Pacific Ocean at the mouth of the Columbia River in November 1805. They constructed Fort Clatsop and hunkered down for the winter in what is now Northwest Oregon. Although no continuous waterway to the Pacific was discovered, Lewis and Clark honed their skills in cartography, documented the practices of over 70 Native American tribes, and described more than 200 new plants and animal species. Their trip was long, treacherous, and laborious. These explorers learned to adapt along the way, and they parlayed their learnings into new skills that allowed their expedition to endure without significant mishaps. In 1806, the Lewis and Clark troupe returned to St. Louis, taking fewer than six months to reach their original starting point in September of that same year. Amazingly, only one person died on this 28-month trek, and, ironically, the suspected cause of Quartermaster Charles Floyd's death was a complicated intraabdominal infection caused by a ruptured appendix. The bugs will get us every time!

I discuss these two journeys today because the road to any discovery, whether in the wilderness or in the laboratory, is never straightforward or easy. Every search for knowledge takes dedication, agility, humility, and courage. The approach taken for any such trek may culminate in success or despair. The two expeditions led by de Soto and Lewis and Clark illustrate this point. The latter expedition conjures up memories of Merck's own quest into the field of HIV research. What started as an endeavor to find a remedy to the AIDS epidemic in the 1980s has led to an historic undertaking. Along the way, knowledge has been gained, new paths have been forged, and a massive change in the care of people living with HIV (PLHIV) has transpired.

The early years of the HIV epidemic were an era of uncertainty, filled with worrisome unrest. It all started in June 1981, when the United States Center for Disease Control and Prevention (CDC) reported five cases of a rare pulmonary infection, *Pneumocystis carinii* pneumonia (PCP), in young, gay men in California. That same day, a dermatologist called the CDC to inform them that he has observed a rare, aggressive malignancy—Kaposi sarcoma (KS)—in several gay men living in New York City. In due time, other opportunistic infections would be reported in similar patient populations, all in the setting of low blood counts and cell-mediated deficiency.

Nearly 15 months later, the CDC would coin the term "AIDS" to describe the syndrome. A little more than two years later, a few French virologists, led by Luc Montagnier, would be credited for discovering the retrovirus, and a group at the NIH, led by Robert Gallo, would link the unchecked replication of the virus to the manifestations of AIDS.

As many in the scientific community bickered over the true discoverer of the virus, millions of individuals became infected with HIV. Yet, by 1984, a group of scientists at Burroughs-Wellcome, including Merck's own Sandi Lehrman, collaborated with scientists at the National Cancer Institute (NCI) to determine that a nucleoside analogue, zidovudine (AZT), was a potent inhibitor of the reverse transcriptase enzyme of HIV. In due time, a double-blind, placebo-controlled trial confirmed a survival advantage for this nucleoside reverse transcriptase inhibitor (NRTI), and AZT was rapidly approved by the FDA in March 1987.

Sadly, the benefit of AZT monotherapy was short-lived, as viral resistance to the NRTI would soon occur, rendering AZT monotherapy ineffective for long-term use.

Merck's role in addressing the HIV epidemic started in late 1986 and has remained steadfast. In December of that year, Dr. Edward Scolnick, the former head of Merck Research Laboratories (MRL), publicly announced that Merck would initiate a comprehensive AIDS research program at our West Point facility. Led by Dr. Emilio Emini, the group of molecular biologists, virologists, and medicinal chemists established the laboratory and targeted the protease enzyme of HIV as a possible pharmaceutical target. They capitalized on prior Merck cardiovascular research on the protease enzyme renin, a known regulator of blood pressure that had been thoroughly interrogated as part of prior research endeavors. In 1988, the research team reported that HIV protease was critical for viral infectivity among CD4 cells. Concurrently, the Merck team elucidated the structure of the protease enzyme. Unfortunately, one of the promising research chemists who played an integral role in its identification, Dr. Irving Sigal, never had a chance to see the 1989 *Nature* publication highlighting the three dimensional structure of the protease enzyme; he was tragically killed in the Libyan terrorist attack on the PanAm Flight 103, while he was traveling home after delivering a talk at a scientific conference in the United Kingdom. Nevertheless, the journey continued forward.

Over the next few years, process researchers and chemists, led by Joe Vacca, Joel Huff, Paul Reider, Bruce Dorsey, and others contrived a new process to synthesize the bulk for a protease inhibitor (PI) lead, referred to as L-735,524. By 1992, safety assessment studies in animals confirmed the tolerability of L-735,524, and, by January 1993, Merck filed an investigational new drug application for this preclinical candidate (then known as MK-639). The next month, the first healthy volunteer trial was initiated with MK-639 at the pharmacokinetic trial unit of Jefferson University Hospital under the auspices of MRL's Paul Deutch. Approximately four months later, a 12-day proof-of-concept trial for MK-639 was begun at the same institution, as well as at University of Alabama-Birmingham, in HIV-infected participants. By the close of 1993, a 6-week trial was also undertaken to interrogate MK-639 doses ranging from 200 to 400 mg every 6 hours (800 to 1600 mg daily) in PLHIV.

Unfortunately, as is often the case in exploration, a setback was encountered when resistance was seen at the lower MK-639 doses. A few patients witnessed a viral load increase of HIV in the blood, despite continued improvement in CD4 count; the finding prompted Merck to reconsider the MK-639 dose. The dose in the Phase 2 trial was increased to 2,400 mg daily (600 mg QID), with subsequent success. All the while, Merck advanced the elegant manufacturing and enhanced the yield of MK-639, now known as indinavir sulfate; indeed, the 15-step process to produce indinavir sulfate was the most sophisticated, complicated chemistry campaign Merck had completed up until that time.

As Phase 3 studies were initiated using a 2,400 mg dose (now at 800 mg TID) in April 1995, Merck also took the risk to begin a capital campaign in Elkton, Virginia, the site of the final manufacturing facility. While the campaign was being completed, the Phase 3 trial (Study 035) randomly assigned about 100 HIV-infected participants who had previously received at least six months of prior AZT therapy to one of three treatment groups: indinavir alone vs. AZT in combination with another new NRTI, lamivudine (3TC) vs. the combination of all three agents. On February 1, 1996, at the third Conference on Retroviruses and Opportunistic Infections (CROI) meeting in Washington DC, Dr. Roy Gulick shared the 24-week data from the trial. In essence, the results demonstrated a 2-log reduction in HIV RNA for the 3-drug treatment group, as compared to only a about 0.5 to 1 log reduction seen in the other two groups. That same day, Merck announced it had submitted an accelerated new drug application (NDA) to the FDA for indinavir sulfate, under the branded name of CRIXIVAN®. Exactly one month later, on March 1, 1996, the FDA Advisory Committee recommended the approval of indinavir, and the FDA responded with a formal approval via the accelerated pathway less than two weeks later. Amazingly, the indinavir approval, which occurred 42 days after the NDA submission, was the fastest FDA approval on record at that time—a tribute to our colleagues at the FDA. That same month, full-scale manufacturing facilities and packaging for a capsule formulation of indinavir were completed within one year of initiation of the Elkton construction site, despite a treacherous winter in Virginia. Indinavir became available for use in late March 1996 as the first 3-drug regimen for HIV infection. All in all, from test tube to final capsule, the indinavir development program would take eight years and cost Merck an estimated $700 million (**Figure 17**).

Although long-term data from Protocol 035 would continue to confirm the durability of the favorable earlier results, the effort was not over. The accelerated approval still necessitated hard endpoint data (as HIV RNA had yet to be accepted as a formal surrogate marker of eventual disease progression to AIDS). To this end, a large, sentinel trial led by the AIDS Clinical Trials Group (ACTG), known as ACTG 320, was initiated in early 2016. That trial enrolled over 1,150 HIV-infected participants to either a 3-drug regimen containing indinavir or a 2-drug NRTI regimen (without indinavir), with the study's primary endpoint focused on either AIDS progression or death. The proportion of subjects progressing to AIDS or death was 6 percent vs. 11 percent, in favor of the 3-drug regimen; the hazard ratio in favor of the 3-drug regimen was impressive at 0.5. These results would eventually support the full approval of indinavir by the FDA.

Of course, indinavir would eventually be replaced with improved, ritonavir-boosted regimens of PI, as their more facile, once-daily administration and lack of adverse complications, such as nephrolithiasis (kidney stones), favored their use over indinavir. Yet, the impact of indinavir, and the demonstration of the need for a 3-drug regimen of highly-active antiretroviral therapy (HAART) that included some anchor agent beyond NRTIs, helped to set a new standard for HIV care.

As a medical student training at Grady Memorial Hospital, the large, publicly-subsidized hospital in Atlanta, Georgia, I vividly remember the sorrowful wards of AIDS patients in the early 1990s. At that time, the only option we had for PLHIV was AZT monotherapy, which was often ineffective for those patients with NRTI-resistant virus. The majority of my patients in my internal medicine rotation suffered from end-stage AIDS. Conditions such as pneumocystis pneumonia (PCP), disseminated Mycobacterium avium complex, cytomegalovirus (CMV) retinitis, and/or AIDS dementia had turned relatively young, healthy men and women into frail, debilitated individuals. I recall filling out my fair share of death certificates, wondering if and when the epidemic might finally abate. Fast forwarding five years to the start of my infectious disease fellowship, I was amazed to witness a phenomenal transformation in patient care. By early 1997, HAART regimens containing CRIXIVAN®, AZT, and 3TC had become commonplace at Massachusetts General Hospital, where I trained, and other major institutions. I remember caring for a 22-year old, cachectic, ventilated man with a CD4 count of nine cells/mm^3 and a severe case of PCP; after the initiation of HAART, he blossomed in six months into a healthy, functioning member of society. I marveled at what companies like Burroughs-Welcome and Merck had done to save his life and the lives of so many infected individuals. I knew that if I were to ever join a career in Industry, Merck would top the list.

Of course, by the time the mid-1990s came to be, Merck had solidified its role in HIV research. But its role in the HIV realm was really just getting started. As Edison once quipped following his ground-breaking discovery of the incandescent light bulb, "When you have exhausted all possibilities, remember this: you haven't."[28] In due time, Merck would help advance the field of non-nucleoside reverse transcriptase inhibitors (NNRTI), with the discovery of efavirenz. By the time Merck and DuPont Pharmaceuticals brought efavirenz to the market in 1998 and the first fixed-dosed combination regimen with efavirenz in 2006, in close collaboration with Gilead Sciences and Bristol-Myers Squibb, the first-line treatment regimen for PLHIV had

---

28 Routinely attributed to Edison but not located in Edison's writings. It is found in Robert H. Schuller's self-help book *Tough Times Never Last, But Tough People Do*.

evolved away from PI-based regimens to the simpler, more convenient NNRTI-based regimens. Merck would propel the field forward again when Daria Hazuda's team brought the first integrase strand transfer inhibitor (InSTI), known as raltegravir, to the market in 2007. In due time, InSTI-based regimens would become the preferred regimens for most PLHIV starting on an antiretroviral treatment (ART) treatment.

Altogether, Merck's collective efforts have altered the trajectory of the HIV epidemic. PLHIV can now live relatively normal lives with six to seven decades of life, provided they adhere to their daily ART regimens. In most developed countries, the mortality associated with HIV has also precipitously fallen, and we've learned that treatment as prevention helps prevent transmission to non-infected partners. Moreover, once-daily regimens to prevent HIV acquisition using pre-exposure prophylaxis (PrEP) are now routinely administered to high-risk populations. Finally, as nicely articulated in the recent *Journal of Infectious Diseases* article by Drs. Tara Schwetz and Anthony Fauci, the collateral benefits to broader scientific progress resulting from the support to HIV/AIDS research have been transformational to the field of virology and medicine as a whole (https://academic.oup.com/jid/article/219/1/6/5063659).

That said, I would be remiss if left the impression that that the 35-year path of HIV research at Merck has been a straightforward venture without its share of challenges. Our efforts to advance an HIV vaccine using a recombinant adenovirus vector did not succeed in preventing HIV infection in the STEP trial, despite the vaccine's demonstrated ability to elicit a strong cellular immune response. Early measures to evaluate raltegravir in the maintenance switch setting (SWITCHMRK) and in the first-line treatment setting as a once-daily regimen (QDMRK) also met with failure. We did eventually crack the once-daily nut for raltegravir with the introduction of a new formulation of raltegravir. Yet, through all our glorious successes and heart-breaking failures in HIV research and development, Merck has remained resolute to the cause.

Why you might ask? The answer is simple: The fight against HIV is far from over.

Since its inception, HIV and AIDS have claimed the lives of over 35 million people—a horrifying statistic. Currently, across the globe, nearly 37 million people live with HIV infection, and nearly two million new infections occur each year. Moreover, nearly one million PLHIV will suffer an AIDS-related death in 2019. To put this in perspective, over 5,000 individuals will be infected today with HIV, and another about 2,750 will die today from AIDS. In the US, we estimate 1.2 million PLHIV, and approximately 40,000 more individuals will contract HIV in 2019. Around the globe and even in the US, we are nowhere close to the UNAIDS 90-90-90 goal of having 90 percent of PLHIV fully diagnosed, 90 percent initiated on ART, and 90 percent with HIV fully suppressed in their blood. Efforts to cure HIV infection are also not on the immediate horizon. For this reason, the WHO appropriately continues to list HIV as one of its top ten threats to global health in 2019.

So, here at Merck, we press on in the quest against HIV.

Today, I'm thankful for all my colleagues in the MRL Early Development organization (DPED), including the Discovery, Preclinical, and Translational Pharmacology arenas, who have helped advance the HIV pipeline forward over the last four decades. I express my profound gratitude to the entire team who remain steadfast in their pursuit of new targets against this epidemic. I also honor and salute those who no longer are with us at Merck who supported this noble cause. I pay special tribute to Dr. Irving Sigal, who sacrificed his life for the mission. Like the great inventors and explorers that we previously discussed, our Merck colleagues in DPED possess a commitment to diligence, an openness to experimentation, and a courage to fail—traits that have already helped stem this tragic epidemic. Today, I'm also grateful that Merck remains one of only three main pharmaceutic companies, along with Gilead Sciences and ViiV Healthcare, still focused in HIV research. I appreciate that our management recognizes that we cannot rest until the war against this epidemic is fully won. So, we'll press on with our 35-year journey through the wilderness until we reach our destination.

In closing, I can only imagine the satisfaction that Lewis and Clark must have felt as they floated down the mouth of the Columbia River and gazed upon the crashing waves of the Pacific Ocean for the first time. I'd like to be there in a similar canoe when we finally crack the scientific code that unlocks the cure to this dreadful disease.

23 A Fondness for the Famous Founding Fathers of Our Fine Family *(June 13, 2019)*

For this week's *Thankful Thursday* segment, I share my fondness for and fascination with our founding fathers who fearlessly fortified our company's fertile foundation. In today's world, it is a rare feat than any institution, whether governmental, academic, or corporate in nature, can proclaim that its fundamental mission has remained steadfast since its inception. Here at Merck, two individuals were instrumental in charting a course that has been unchanged since its origin. These men laid the cornerstone for the success of a new industry, and, in the process, changed the health and wellbeing of humanity. They also shared the same DNA, the same name, and the same household. Today, I pay homage to George F. Merck and his son, George W. Merck.

Let me begin by wishing everyone a wonderful Father's Day three days early. This coming Sunday, the third in the month of June, is the United States's 53rd celebration of Father's Day—a day in honor of dads and the influence of fatherhood in our society. First issued as a national proclamation by President Lyndon B. Johnson in 1966, Father's Day became a formal, national holiday when it was signed into law by President Richard Nixon in 1972. This year, more than 75 million fathers in the United Sates will celebrate the day with GTT. No, GTT is not that ominous system into which your diligent Merck managers plead with you to enter your weekly hours, but rather an acronym for the three items that best symbolize fatherhood: golf, tools, and ties. When I first envisioned this chapter, I planned to dedicate its entirety to these three different topics, but, as I've noted below, I ultimately decided against it for a variety of reasons:

- Father's Day is traditionally the last day of the US Open in golf—the most democratic, competitive tournament in sports (as the amateur golfer Roy McAvoy so eloquently boasted to his psychiatrist in the movie, *Tin Cup*). Recognized as one of the four Major Professional Golf Association Championships in golf, the US Open has been in existence since 1895, longer than most major sporting championships in this country. Several years ago, I had the unique privilege of attending the US Open at Merion in Ardmore, Pennsylvania, where the challenging course stymied the golfers' performances. The atmosphere was so much fun! Frankly, I would encourage my colleagues out in San Diego to partake in this year's tournament in Pebble Beach if you have the time and a few thousand dollars to waste. I am a weekend golf enthusiast, but I decided against sharing my gratitude for this great game in this week's chapter because, frankly, golf is just too damn humbling. Just when I'm convinced that I've finally figured out my swing, my patented slice. which defies at least three fundamental laws of physics, rears its ugly head. No wonder Mark Twain referred to golf as "a good walk spoiled,"[29] and the Australian golfer Greg Norman summed it up as the most vulgar 4-letter word in the entire English dictionary. Whenever I play this humbling game, I find it to be something akin to an act of self-flagellation. So, it should not come as a surprise to discover that that when you spell the word "golf" backwards, you get "flog." So, a dedicated segment to golf is *not* up to par.
- A time-honored myth is the notion that all a man really wants for Father's Day is a gift certificate to *Home Depot* so he can buy the latest Ridgid® power tool or computerized gadget. Well, to all those folks contemplating a *Lowe's* gift certificate as a Father's Day present for your benevolent, endearing dads, let me offer up two simple words of advice: Please don't. When I was growing up in the Kartsonis household, my father never paid anyone to fix a problem until we as a family had a first crack at it. Speaking of cracks, it was sheer blasphemy to think that we would ever

29 Routinely attributed to Mark Twain but first used in 1948 in *The Saturday Evening Post* of August 1948. Twain died in 1910 and there is no mention of it in his writings.

pay a plumber to fix a cracked pipe. My father deemed it one of seven cardinal sins to have to call a professional to fix a broken appliance prior to us first trouble-shooting the problem. As a teenager in Jacksonville, Florida, I still remember one blistering hot summer when we suffered in sweltering silence without air conditioning for three solid days in August because my father was convinced we could troubleshoot the compressor problem. Well, we couldn't, despite my father's assiduity, technical acumen, and can-do-attitude. Defeated and dejected, he sauntered into the kitchen, dialed the local HVAC specialist on our rotary phone, and went back to the family room to wait, all the while watching some monotonous episode of the "Lawrence Welk Show."

Incidentally, my father routinely encouraged me to play the accordion, a regular feature on the Lawrence Welk Show. There was no way on this earth that I was going to play that silly instrument, so I bucked by playing the trumpet in the Third Grade Band. At the end of that school year, the music teacher called me into his office and encouraged me to find another hobby, as my skills at horn blowing were extremely pathetic. He effectively ended my career as an aspiring musician. But, I digress.

Over the years, my family and friends have bestowed upon me several tools as Father's Day presents, including a hammer with an awesome red Phillies emblem adorned on the side. I'm not sure I need it, but I now definitely own it. My handyman skills would suggest that such a gift is wasted on me. Case in point: A few weeks ago, I tried to remove a garden hose from a spigot on the side of our house using a monkey wrench because the hose would not budge using just my bare hands. Well, I was able to extract the hose from the side of my house, but I also removed the entire spigot from the wall—with the hose still tied to the spigot. So, I would be terribly disingenuous if I claimed to be a true handyman and chose to focus today's *Thankful Thursday* segment on tools.

- So, that leaves me with neckties. How can anyone not hold in high esteem the most popular gift on Father's Day? I contemplated writing an entire segment on how the tie has played a crucial role throughout history, ultimately revolutionizing men's fashion. Did you know that the modern necktie goes back to Louis XIV, the great French Sun King? In the early seventeenth century,

> mercenaries from Croatia were brought to Paris to fight on France's behalf in the Thirty Years War. Croatian soldiers adorned themselves with these small, knotted neck garments, which the French populace colloquially referred to as *"cravats"* to parody the French term for Croatians (*Croates*). The boy king was so enamored with these lace neckerchiefs that he started to wear them in public, and soon all the French nobility and most of Europe's elite were mimicking his practice as a social sign of elegance, civility, and wealth. Unfortunately, by the time of the Industrial Revolution, most men had grown weary of the cravat because of its lack of comfort and convenience. Cravats were not only complicated to tie in a knot, but the knot also tended to come undone as the day wore on. In time, the modern-day necktie, with its long, thin appearance, became popular. One silly fact I uncovered is that several scientists at Cambridge University in the United Kingdom have used mathematical modeling to discover that one can tie a conventional necktie into 85 unique knots, including my favorite, the *Nicky Knot.* Today, ties have fallen out of favor for a variety of reasons. Some have discovered the hard way that it is probably best not to wear a necktie while operating heavy equipment, chasing after a criminal, or working as a prison guard. Additionally, recent studies suggest that neckties may even result in increased intraocular pressure or vascular constriction if worn too taut. Finally, as an infectious disease physician, I must advise that neckties are incredibly efficient vectors for microbial transmission, to the point that some medical institutions have banned their staff from wearing neckties while on the hospital wards. So, a dissertation on neckties for this week's *Thankful Thursday segment* would just get me all tangled up in knots.

I also contemplated sharing my gratitude for some of the great "fathers" in history. As the first true Renaissance man, Leonardo Da Vinci came immediately to mind. His masterpieces on canvas and his intense curiosity for invention helped humankind achieve a new level of enlightenment, after nearly a millennium of the Dark Ages. I even pondered acknowledging the Father of the Scientific Revolution, Sir Isaac Newton. His creation of the modern telescope, his elucidation of the laws of motion and of gravity, and his advancement of the field of mathematics (including the birth of calculus) have raised Newton into the echelons of my scientific heroes. Finally, I thought about waxing poetic about a worthy historical figure and the subject of my favorite song in the *Hamilton* musical—the venerable George Washington. As one of our nation's founding fathers, as well as the Father of the American Revolution, Washington went on to become the United States' first President, ultimately setting a legacy of moral integrity, a standard for civil discourse, and the precedence of limited political power—the latter of which I am most grateful. Yet, none in this trio of great "fathers" ever sired a child. Thus, I found it a bit odd to shower them with my profuse praise and ardent appreciation on this day dedicated to dutiful dads.

So, then it came to me. Why not share the story of the two fathers of our great company? With this in mind, let's get to know these two men a bit more, so I can convince you of their worthiness for today's *Thankful Thursday* praise.

As I previously described in my lighthearted chapter about the wonderful state of New Jersey, Merck has its roots in a small town in Germany called Darmstadt. Back in 1668, Friedrich Jacob Merck purchased a small apothecary called "At the Sign of the Angel Pharmacy," which was situated at the foot of a large castle. The retail store remained unchanged in the family for six generations before one of its descendants, Heinrich Emmanuel Merck, transformed the pharmacy into a chemical/pharmaceutical factory in 1827. Among the outputs of what had become E. Merck AG (now known as Merck KGaA—the oldest pharmaceutical entity in existence) were products such as morphine, codeine, and cocaine. Heinrich passed the company down to his son, Wilhelm Merck, who continued to lead E. Merck AG into the early twentieth century. Near the end of the nineteenth century, amid the Industrial Revolution, Wilhelm recognized the potential of establishing a subsidiary in the United States; he also worried about counterfeit products which bore the E. Merck AG name showing up in the United States. So, Wilhelm sent one of his officers, Theodore Weiker, to New York City in 1887 to establish a sales office at 62 Wall Street. Recognizing the need for more support, Weiker petitioned the Merck family to send reinforcements, so Wilhelm sent over the youngest of his two sons, the 24-year-old George Friedrich Merck to assist in the campaign in 1891 (**Figure 18**). Now, George was a learned, well-traveled individual, having studied in Germany, France, and Canada. In fact, he even completed a 3-year apprenticeship in Frankfurt as a drug wholesaler and businessman. Together, Weiker and Merck successfully grew the business to the point that they recognized the need to set up their own industrial site in the United States. In

1899, they purchased 150 rural acres in Rahway, New Jersey, and four years later, the site was actively manufacturing chemicals and pharmaceuticals. At that same time, George gained his US citizenship and started a family in Llewellyn Park, a rolling hill suburb of West Orange, with his wife, Friedrike. Together, George and Friedrike had five children, including their oldest, George W. Merck, who was born in 1894 (**Figure 19**).

When Theodore Weiker left the company to form his own pharmaceutical entity—E. R. Squibb & Sons, now part of Bristol-Myers Squibb—George F. Merck assumed the command of the Merck United States operation in 1904. As his family grew, so did the Merck enterprise in the States. His biggest challenge came in 1917, when President Wilson and the United States were thrust into World War I. Despite being a US citizen, George feared the rising anti-German sentiment. Thus, he readily complied when the US government forced him to sever ties with the German branch of the family business, E. Merck AG. He voluntarily transferred a large portion of Merck stock, 80 percent of the total share and the entirety of the E. Merck AG holdings, over to the Alien Property Custodian of the United States. In doing so, any connection of his corporate subsidiary to the German parent company, E. Merck AG, was permanently severed, and the new company became its own private entity. After the war, the US government opted to sell the Merck stock at a public auction. Acting quickly, despite his disappointment with the US Alien Property Custodian's decision to take the company public, George received the financial support of two banks, Goldman Sachs and Lehman Brothers, to outbid the other four potential buyers at the auction. George had his company back but at a hefty price for the time, about $3.75 million. After a formal agreement was signed forbidding the German E. Merck AG from having any undue influence over the company, the new Merck Corporation became a public entity with George as its president. In signing the agreement, George cut all family ties with his father's enterprise in Germany. George continued to lead The Merck Corporation for another six years until 1925, at which point he handed off the company to his oldest son, George W. Merck, while the elder Merck became Chairman of the Board. By that time, the Merck Corporation had grown into a large chemical and pharmaceutical entity, predominantly manufacturing antiseptics and disinfectants. As the facility in Rahway blossomed into a bona fide factory, the company's value increased to $6 million.

So, what about the new president, George W. Merck (GWM)?

His story is even more fascinating. Born the oldest of five siblings into an affluent family situated in the suburbs of West Orange, New Jersey, GWM benefitted from his father's prestige and recognition. As a child, GWM had ready access to Thomas A. Edison's West Orange laboratory, where he often hobnobbed with the great inventor and his two sons, who were close childhood friends of GWM. Thomas Edison developed a strong connection to GWM, even routinely referring to him facetiously as "Shorty" (probably because GWM, at a height of 6 feet, 5 inches, was towering over the short inventor). These early interactions with the inventor inspired in GWM an innovative, inquisitive mindset. Following his graduation from the Dearborn-Morgan School, he enrolled in the Harvard University in 1915, where he majored in chemistry. Always a bit of a jokester, he edited the *Harvard Lampoon*. Nonetheless, he never viewed his studies as a laughing matter; in fact, he graduated a year early, ahead of his classmates, in 1918. Although GWM hoped to further his education with a chemistry doctorate degree in Germany, World War I unfortunately prohibited this educational pursuit. Instead, he joined his father's company. Over the next seven years, he familiarized himself with every aspect of the business, serving time in nearly every department. Finally, in 1925, he became the president of The Merck Foundation Company, as his father, George F. Merck, turned his attention to the Merck Board. Although he hoped to glean continued wisdom from his father, such a wish was not granted, as his father, whose health had declined, died a year later at the relatively young age of 59.

Now, at the age of 32, GWM was alone, at the helm of a growing enterprise. However, he recognized that moss does not gather on a rolling stone. So, in 1927 GWM merged Merck with the Powers-Weightman-Rosengarten Company, a Philadelphia-based fine chemical company that was best known for its mass production of quinine, an antimalarial agent. The merger was a critical undertaking, as the Merck Foundation, despite its improving financial situation, was still heavily mortgaged after the 1919 auction. Fortunately, the four Rosengarten brothers, led by the oldest, Adolph, were looking for a buyout, and

GWM was looking to ensure Merck's solvency. The new company, known as Merck and Co., Inc., was born.[30]

A few years later, GWM made an even bolder move when he transformed the entire pharmaceutical industry by establishing a laboratory where pure and applied research could be undertaken on par with that of the great, academic universities in the United States. Taking a page from Edison's book, he created a campus-like atmosphere in Rahway to lure prominent chemists, biologists, and chemical engineers to Merck. For the first time, this new laboratory housed the three research arms of the company—Merck Institute of Therapeutic Research, the Laboratory for Pure and Fundamental Research, and the Laboratory of Applied Research—under a single roof. At the opening ceremony of the laboratory in 1933 (**Figure 20**), GWM would proclaim: "We have the faith that in this new laboratory, with the tools we have supplied, science will be advanced, knowledge increased, and human life will win ever a greater freedom from suffering and disease." He partnered with the American Chemical Society to facilitate a program to attract aspiring scientists to a career in Industry. Luminaries like Randolph Major, the first head of the research labs, Karl Folkers, and Max Tishler would join Merck. Over the next two decades, these men helped the Rahway labs synthesize sulfa-based drugs, cortisone, and numerous vitamins, including B_1, B_2, B_5, B_6, and B_{12}, the last of which would effectively cure pernicious anemia. By 1941, a large Stonewall manufacturing facility in Elkton, Virginia, was already in operation to mass produce the wide assortment of drug products conceived at the Rahway research labs.

But, then war struck in 1941. Sadly, Merck was already in the midst of the controversies of the conflict. Most of the quinine for their antimalarial agent was derived from the bark of the cinchona tree in the Dutch East Indies. Anticipating the potential occupation by Japan, Merck extracted the large supply of bark from Java, Sumatra,

30 Incidentally, if you itch to experience the opulence of the Rosengarten family, I'd suggest you spend a day at Chanticleer Gardens, the 48-acre botanical garden built at the Adolph Rosengarten summer home in Wayne, Pennsylvania. The grounds at the estate are absolutely stunning—not surprisingly, the estate is on the US National Register of Historic Places. If you visit, don't forget to check out the Dollhouse behind the original Chanticleer house, the Asian Woods, the Vegetable Garden, and the "Ruins'!

and other Asia Pacific regions and gave it directly to the United States government. Consequently, the company established plantations of the cinchona tree in Guatemala to secure the uninterrupted supply of this important drug to the Allied troops.

Merck's real involvement in the war effort is tied to its role in the mass production of penicillin. The technical capabilities for the production of penicillin were transferred in 1939 from Oxford University in the United Kingdom to the Northern Regional Research Laboratory (NRRL) in Peoria, Illinois. Under the supervision of Norman Heatley and Howard Florey, who had both emigrated from the United Kingdom to the United States, the NRRL team in Peoria were beginning to tackle the challenges of the large-scale production of penicillin. In addition to the use of the *P. chrysogenum* strain isolated from the mold-infested cantaloupe from the Peoria market, the yield of penicillin was increased by the use of lactose in lieu of sucrose, phenylacetic acid, and corn-steep liquor. As aeration was needed to enhance the fermentation process, oxygen was continuously pumped into the media to agitate the fungus to mass produce the penicillin by-product.

While these advances were taking place, Heatley met with a confidante from the University of Pennsylvania, Alfred N. Richards, in an effort to spark national interest in penicillin production. GWM and Richards were close confidantes—in fact, Richards was instrumental in luring Randolph Major away from Princeton University to help the research efforts at Merck. Richards coordinated a first meeting with all the key pharmaceutical companies in Washington DC in October 1941, which was attended by Randolph Major and the leaders from three other major pharmaceutical companies at the time—Squibb, Pfizer, and Lilly. Major reported back to GWM about the meeting, but GWM was skeptical of the progress in Peoria; GWM was concerned that the use of the corn-steep liquor was an inefficient method for fermentation. Nevertheless, GWM tagged along with Randolph to the next meeting mid-December 1941 with Heatley and the other companies.

By this time, something profound had transpired.

Ten days earlier, the bombing of Pearl Harbor had galvanized the United States to enter the Allied war effort. As GWM listened to the progress in penicillin fermentation at Peoria, he immediately changed his pessimistic tune and said: "If the results could be confirmed in our laboratories and indeed have the potential to produce kilos of material, we will do it!" The pilot plant in Rahway got busy producing several hundred liters of penicillin, and Norman Heatley joined Merck for several months to help optimize the fermentation process. By March 1942, Merck had generated enough penicillin to treat a patient in New Haven, Connecticut, the first ever treated in the United States, followed by another ten patients in June with success. Over the next year, the fermentation, extraction, and purification steps were enhanced, thanks to the support of scientists at Merck, Pfizer, Lederle, and Squibb (**Figure 21**). The four key companies and others continued to mass produce the antibiotic at their facilities under the watchful supervision of the War Production Board (WPB). In 1943 alone, Merck produced 4.18 billion units of penicillin. War-time patriotism inspired the workers at each of the manufacturers. As the leader of the WPB effort, Albert Enders, described it to GWM and others: "You are urged to impress upon every worker in your plant that the penicillin produced today will be saving the life of someone in a few days or curing the disease of someone now incapacitated. Put up slogans in your plant! Place notices in pay envelopes! Create an enthusiasm for the job down to the lowest worker in your plant!" GWM followed suit, and the mass production skyrocketed. Between 1943 and 1945, penicillin production increased from 21 billion units to 6.8 trillion units. Enough penicillin was made to support the entire D-Day Operation in 1944 and the remainder of the war effort in Europe and Asia Pacific (**Figure 22**). All the while, GWM also co-led the Research Service overseeing the US Biologics Weapons division. Even in these times of significant stress, GWM never lost his temper, joked endlessly with his colleagues, and inspired family, friends, and colleagues with endless encouragement, a feeling of security, and inspiration.

This, my friends, is what we call inspirational leadership.

GWM gave up his post as the President of Merck in 1950, handing over the reins to James J. Kerrigan, so he could spend more time with his wife, five children, and grandchildren at their homes in New Jersey, Vermont, and Florida. Yet he remained active as the Chairman of the Merck Board and he continued to participate in goodwill efforts. GWM served as the president of Manufacturing Chemists Association and on Eisenhower's board of the National Science Foundation until his death at the age of 63 in 1957 from a cerebral hemorrhage. Several years later, his family donated the surrounding acreage around their home in Vermont to create the *Merck Forest and Farmland Foundation*, a public-use land dedicated to forest agriculture and sustainable farming.

So today, I take a moment to reflect on our company's two founding fathers, George F. and George W. Merck. Their vision, strategic thinking, and down-to-earth approach laid the foundation for our company as a premier research-driven pharmaceutical entity—a mission we embrace to this day. I also am grateful for all our "dads" who've led Merck over time, including Mr. Kerrigan, Connor, Gadsen, Horan, Vagelos, Gilmartin, Clark, and Frazier. It is amazing to think that in the 128-year history of Merck in the United States, we have witnessed only ten leaders at our company's helm. The first two of these men, both named George Merck, ruled for 59 of those 128 years.

Of course, I'm also immensely grateful for my own father, who took pride in his role as a family man. As someone who was destitute when he emigrated to the United States in 1959, my dad embodied the work ethic, tenacity, and hopeful spirit espoused by all immigrants. Although he's not with us anymore, I remember him this week for all he taught me about life and the skills required to be an attentive father to my own three sons. I see my dad's resemblance in my youngest son, Jack, and the striking similarity triggers a memory that always makes me smile.

In closing, Happy Father's Day to all of you dads out there celebrating this upcoming Sunday. May you have a relaxing day manning a grill, watching the final round of the US Open, or hiking in the woods (perhaps a trip to Merck Forest?). I'll probably stay home and shoot some hoops with Jack and my other sons in our back yard—and try not to hurt myself. And, when my kids hand me a colorful necktie from Vineyard Vines® or a new power drill from Lowe's as a Father's Day present, I'll just sit back, smile, and say: "Thank you so much for thinking of me."[31]

31 All quotes from George W. Merck and Albert Enders within this essay were identified in various Merck Archives, held by Heritage Werks, Inc.

24 The Magnificent Merck Manual of Materia Medica *(June 20, 2019)*

For this week's *Thankful Thursday* segment, I'd like to convey my gratitude for a noble initiative our company embarked on 120 years ago. Since 1899, Merck has published *The Merck Manual*, a comprehensive medical resource for health care professionals. *The Merck Manual* has been acknowledged as the oldest continuously published general medical text in the English language. Through the years, Merck has stayed with its mission of providing this book on a not-for-profit basis as a service to the medical community and our patients.

Before we delve into a discussion of the tremendous value of *The Merck Manual*, I want to share with you three fun facts about June 20, and why I opted to pay homage to the book on this particular day.

First, the third week of June in the Northern Hemisphere is a time when the Earth has its maximal tilt to the sun, thereby permitting the sun to reach its highest position in the sky. Hence, north of the Equator, the year's longest 24-hour period of daylight is maintained, including continuous light for the entire day in certain northern-most regions of the globe. Referred to as the Summer Solstice, this natural phenomenon is marked with celebratory festivals, ritualistic holidays, and the occasional cry of an ensuing Armageddon. Nevertheless, each year, we all survive, ensuring that the next year's Summer Solstice can once again occur sometime between June 20 and 22. Technically, the 2019 Summer Solstice occurs tomorrow, June 21, 2019. Around the Northern Hemisphere, inhabitants will celebrate the Summer

Solstice with the Dragon Boat Festival in various parts of Eastern Asia, the Juhannus festival in Finland, and the Jani celebration in Latvia. The Summer Solstice celebration also marks World Music Day, International Surfing Day, and, International Yoga Day. So, *namaste* to you all! Turn on the Beach Boys, grab your surfboard, and head for the beach (after you've first stood on your head for three minutes)!

Second, June twentieth also marks the anniversary of the establishment of the Great Seal of the United States. In a prior *Thankful Thursday* segment about Martin Luther King Jr., I told how a committee was commissioned on July 4, 1776, to design a national emblem for our new nation. Although our country was only a few hours old at the time of its commissioning, our forefathers knew the importance of having an official symbol of sovereignty for our new nation. Unfortunately, agreement on a design would be a somewhat painful process that lasted as long as the entire American Revolution. After six years of debate, three separate committees, and the contributions of 14 individuals, the seal would finally be approved by the Continental Congress on June 20, 1782. (This contentious, time-consuming process forebode how the United States Congress would operate for the next 230-plus years). The design approved in 1782 was actually envisaged by the Secretary of the Congress, Charles Thompson. He took elements of the previously-rejected designs and melded them into a symbolic design, and he did so in just one week's time. The Great Seal of the United States is still in use today on treaty documents, passports, military insignia, embassy placards, and the one-dollar bill. Thompson has a near and dear place in my heart, as he resided just a few miles from me at the Bryn Mawr House, now known as Harriton House. The town where the building still stands, Bryn Mawr, and my sons' high school, Harriton High, pay tribute to his historic effort.

Finally, June 20 commemorates the day the United States and the Union of Soviet Socialist Republics (USSR) agreed to set up a system to allow direct communication between the two world superpowers. On June 20, 1963, the two nations met in Geneva, Switzerland, and agreed to establish the Washington-Moscow hotline, a direct portal linking the Pentagon and the Kremlin. The hotline was borne out of the near disastrous events leading up to 1962 Cuban Missile Crisis. During that contested standoff, official diplomatic messages took somewhere between 6 to 12 hours to deliver and decipher, unnecessarily escalating the tensions between these two nations. The new hotline agreement initially used teletype equipment to transmit messages between the two nations. Over time, the hotline technology evolved with the use of fax machines and secure computer links, where hourly messages are exchanged via email. Despite popular myth, the hotline was never maintained as a red telephone.

In summary, June 20 is a day we celebrate the longest day, the founding of a historic emblem, and the creation of a critical lifeline. How fitting then that we now turn our attention to a venerable emblem that has readily served as a hotline through the test of time—*The Merck Manual*!

Back in the late 1890s, one of our company's founding fathers, George F. Merck, supported the idea of creating a clinical reference for the medical community. Tailored specifically for physicians and pharmacists, *The Merck Manual of the Materia Medica* was an alphabetical compendium of all known symptoms, signs, and diseases, as well as an easily-accessible resource listing all known compounds with beneficial or therapeutic properties for treating these conditions. Divided into three easily navigated parts, this 192-page pocket-sized guide sold for just one dollar. This low price set forth the still-existing policy that the book's publication is not intended for commercial gain but rather to provide a non-profit service to the medical community in need. If you've never had a chance to read the original 1899 version, I'd suggest you go on Amazon, purchase a facsimile copy of the original version, and then carve out some time to peruse this masterpiece (**Figure 23**). Its front page proclaims its mission:

> "MERCK'S MANUAL is designed to meet a need which every general practitioner has often experienced. Memory is treacherous. It is particularly so with those who have much to do and more to think of. When the best remedy is wanted, to meet indications in cases that are a little out of the usual run, it is difficult, and sometimes impossible, to recall the whole array of available remedies so as to pick out the best. Strange to say, too, it is the most thoroughly informed man that is likely to suffer to the greatest extent in this way; because of the very fact that his mind is overburdened. But a mere reminder is all he needs, to make him at once master of the situation and enable him to prescribe exactly what his judgment tells him is needed for the occasion. In MERCK'S MANUAL, the physician will find a complete Ready-Reference Book covering the entire eligible Materia Medica. A

> glance over it just before or just after seeing a patient will refresh his memory in a way that will facilitate his coming to a decision."

OK, I readily admit that the Introduction is a bit dramatic. Nevertheless, it is undeniably entertaining. The pages that follow provide a riveting historic glimpse into what the pharmaceutical care of patients looked like just over a century ago. This earliest version contains references to drugs still in modern practice, such as digitalis for heart failure, colchicine for gout, bismuth salts for gastrointestinal maladies, and salicylates for headache or fever. Some of the remedies to treat common conditions are "epic" or "lit," as my teenage sons would say. The original Manual recommended tobacco to cure nymphomania, and the "delights of a Turkish bath" to subdue the "malaise after dining out." Frightening as it may seem, poisonous compounds, such as arsenic, mercury, lead, and strychnine, are featured to treat conditions such as anemia, hydrophobia, and impotence. Nevertheless, the editors realized this first version was not perfect, and even acknowledged as much on the cover: "Physicians are earnestly requested to communicate to Merck & Co., University Place, New York, any suggestions that may tend to improve this book for its Second Edition, which will soon be in course of preparation. Whatever the Publishers can do to make Merck's Manual of still greater service to the Medical Profession will be gladly undertaken and promptly performed for all subsequent editions. Therefore, any Physician who will propose improvements in the subject-matter (especially as regards the Newer Materia Medica), or in the arrangement, style, and form of this work, for future editions, will thus be rendering valuable service, not only to its Publishers, but to the entire Profession as well!"

Over the next 120 years, *The Merck Manual* would continue to improve. Merck's general intent was to publish a new edition at least once every five years, and *The Merck Manual* has kept true to this mission ever since. With a few exceptions due to extenuating circumstances—shortage of paper during World War I, the destitute condition caused by the Stock Market crash, and the limited personnel as a result of World War II—*The Merck Manual* has been updated every five or six years. Along the way, many of its Editors-in-Chief, including Dr. M.R. Dinkespiel , Robert Berkow, and Robert Porter, improved subsequent editions, with each successive version becoming larger in size and scope (**Figure 24**).

The modern manual is now organized into 24 organ systems, with each section covering a summary of diagnosis, prognosis, and treatment. The more recent versions are carefully structured into bite-size amounts of information, with clear headers and subheaders, the use of bullets and other easy-to-follow structural techniques, and a *Key Points* section summarizing outstanding features. The *Manual* was never intended to be an all-encompassing bible for pathophysiology and clinical care. Rather, it's an excellent starting place on the road to medical knowledge, with its practical, straightforward tips to diagnosis and treatment. In addition to the main version, *The Merck Manual of Diagnosis and Therapy*, separate manuals have been tailored specifically for medical students and other healthcare professionals in training (*The Merck Manual of Patient Symptoms*) as well as for consumers (*The Merck Manual of Medical Information—Home Edition* and *The Merck Go-To Home Guide for Symptoms)*. A version focused on geriatric care has also been written for professionals (*The Merck Manual of Geriatrics*) and consumers (*The Merck Manual of Health and Aging*). There are even animal health equivalents for veterinarians and pet owners (*The Merck Veterinary Manual* and *The Merck/Merial Manual for Pet Health,* respectively). All in all, seven different versions of the *Merck Manual* are available in print and digital formats.

As a tribute to each of these seven versions, I thought it might be fun to share seven pieces of trivia about *The Merck Manual.*

1. *The Merck Manual* has been long regarded as a renowned, premier reference for instantaneous knowledge at one's fingertips. As proof to its usefulness as a resource, Dr. Albert Schweitzer, the famed physician and theologian who spearheaded a hospital mission in Gabon, Africa, in 1913, kept a handy copy in his pocket. Even the explorer, Admiral Richard E. Byrd, carried the guide with him during his 1929 exploration of Antarctica. I can picture him staying up all night during the Southern Hemisphere's *Summer Solstice*—December 21—reading his trusted *Manual*!
2. In the past, *The Merck Manual* has been regarded as the world's best-selling medical textbook. The guide is available in 17 different languages, including Arabic, Chinese, Japanese, Russian, and, of course, Greek.
3. Twenty editions of *The Merck Manual* have been published in print. In 2014, the company decided to move *The Merck Manual* to a digital-only format; however, that decision was reversed in

2017, leading to the printed publication of the twentieth edition last year. A printed version is still deemed as valuable, recognizing there remain countless places in the world with limited electronic connectivity. Moreover, for someone like me who prefers the tactile sensation and personal satisfaction of holding a book in his hand, I enjoy having my trusted print version of *The Merck Manual* by my side, just like I did when I was a medical student, a resident, and an infectious disease fellow.

4. With the evolution of digital technology, *The Merck Manual* is now available free of charge on the internet (www.merckmanuals.com). In addition, apps with complete downloadable content are available in different languages—once again, free of charge. The digital information is continuously updated to ensure as the information is as accurate as possible. Access to the app is available without any registration, and its use is unlimited, unlike many other medical reference guides. All digital versions are devoid of any advertisement or promotional components. As testimony to its value, *The Merck Manual* website receives, on average, one million visitors each day! Separate versions are kept up to date in at least nine different languages for both the health-care professional and the consumer. This approach is consistent with the fundamental mission to provide information to inform medical decisions and improve the lives of patients worldwide without attention to corporate gain. Merck maintains the belief that health information is a right that every person is entitled to; it should be practical, accurate, and easily accessible.
5. As part of an ambitious goal, *The Merck Manual* staff has committed to a new initiative, *Global Medical Knowledge 2020*. The endeavor strives to make the best current medical information accessible to three billion professionals and patients by 2020. As such, all translations to *The Merck Manuals* will be made available online and kept current with the English version. In those regions with limited digital access, *The Merck Manual* staff maintain outreach programs to facilitate the availability of its printed version. Through partnerships like *Books for Africa*, Merck has donated over 200,000 copies of the professional and consumer editions to non-governmental organizations for distribution to physicians, nurses, pharmacists, and community health workers in the developing world.

6. The company published the twentieth edition of *The Merck Manual* in 2018. The 13th edition, published in 1977, was the first to be published using IBM punch cards and magnetic tape. Prior to that, all versions were prepared on a typewriter. The 12th version, published in 1972, was typed entirely by a single person.
7. Although the editorial staff for *The Merck Manual* is employed by Merck and Co., Inc., the more than 300 expert authors of its content are not employed by Merck, and the independent editorial board of more than 20 members and peer reviewers cannot work for Merck, serve as company speakers, nor represent the company in any other way. The Merck editorial staff has no control, review, or influence on the medical content contained within its resource. Hence, *The Merck Manual* is a trusted, unbiased assessment of the latest medical information, without influence from Merck or the pharmaceutical industry as a whole.

All in all, I hope I've been able to convey to you my admiration of Merck's unrelenting commitment to *The Merck Manual. The Manual's* longevity is profound, and its role as a universal resource of concise, complete, and current information is admirable. In addition, as a hotline to the most up-to-date information for a particular condition, the *Merck Manual* is that proverbial red phone which you can pick up at any time of need.

So, today, I'm thankful to all the folks in Robert Porter's group who help to support the endeavor known as the *Merck Manuals*. Rob's team provides critical editorial support to *The Merck Manual.* Additionally, many others within the group are integral in keeping the legacy alive, whether it is in support of the *Manual's* daily operations, the slew of publishing or digital activities tied with the *Manual*, or the periodic updates of the seven versions of the *Manual*. The group overseeing the *Manual* also works to reinvent itself—akin to how my favorite band, The Beatles, reinvented themselves many years ago by assuming an alter ego—The Sgt. Pepper's Lonely Hearts Club Band—during their production of the epic album of the same name. I love that album so much, as many of you already know.

Finally, I'm thankful to George F. Merck and his colleagues who had the vision, foresight, and wisdom to start something so great. I readily admit that I've relied heavily on my *Merck Manual* since the days of my medical school training. And, yes, I still thumb through my printed version in my office when I need to brush up on a medical condition.

At over 3,300 pages, the latest edition of the *Merck Manual* does not fit snugly in my pocket. Fortunately , however, my trusted iPhone does, and I can turn to it and the useful *Merck Manual* app whenever I'm on the go, stuck in a painful meeting, or just passing time.

George F. Merck was right. Memory is treacherous, especially for an overburdened mind. Sometimes, it's critical to get by with a little help from my friends.

Now, where have I heard that phrase before?

25 The Munificence and Mindfulness of My Magnificent Mentors *(June 27, 2019)*

For this week's *Thankful Thursday* segment, I marvel at those magnificent mentors who've managed to make a marked impact on me. Over my career, I've been fortunate to receive advice, guidance, and wisdom from many experts. By graciously affording me their time and energy, these individuals have provided me with practical skills, technical know-how, and staunch courage to succeed in my career, even in the face of seemingly insurmountable obstacles.

So, today we pay tribute to mentors. But, what exactly defines a mentor? From where does this term derive?

We need to embark on a journey back in time to my motherland, where we will seek answers to these questions. Of all the playwrights, historians, and authors who lived in the times of ancient Greece, the one giant who stands out above all the rest is Homer, the author of the two epic poems about the Trojan War and its immediate aftermath. As the wonderful storyteller of *The Iliad* and *The Odyssey,* Homer can provide us with answers to our inquiries. As the tales go, the King of the Greek island of Ithaca, Odysseus, left his homeland to join other Greeks in their fight against the city-state of Troy. Desperately seeking to restore honor to the Spartan throne and their king, Menelaus, whose beautiful wife Helen was kidnapped by the handsome Trojan warrior Paris, Odysseus joined the war effort. He entrusted his entire household to his faithful friend Mentor. Mentor assumed the task of educating Odysseus's son, the young prince of Ithaca, Telemachus.

After a grueling battle that lasted a decade, the Greeks prevailed against the Trojans with the help of some ingenuity and a large wooden horse. However, Odysseus' attempt to return to his beloved Ithaca after the victory would result in 10-year journey. In retaliation for the Greek army's destruction of the religious temples during the battle of Troy, the Greek Gods punished Odysseus by taking him on a life-altering journey. They set a decade-long course that made Odysseus wander the seas aimlessly with his crew from one adventure to another. His son, Telemachus, was becoming a sophisticated adult, having been educated by the elder Mentor. Feeling sorry for Odysseus, the Goddess of Wisdom, Athena, assumes the body of Mentor and coaxes Telemachus to embark on a journey to find his long-lost father. So, Telemachus sets off on a quest to find his father, all the while being guided by Athena under the guise of Mentor. Eventually, father and son are reunited, and the two return to reclaim Ithaca from suitors who had usurped the throne from Telemachus and his mother, Penelope. As the king is now 20 years older than he was when he departed Ithaca, no one recognizes him when he returns—that is, except for his trusty canine, Argos. He has also disguised himself as a beggar. Although Argos is excited to see his owner, his exuberance causes the poor old dog to collapse and die. Fortunately, his master's disguise is not revealed. (As someone who has an insatiable love of dogs, it aches me to write this story down. Nevertheless, it affords you a true appreciation of how Homer and the Greek playwrights really knew how to pierce a sword through someone's heart!) Of course, Odysseus and Telemachus succeed in disposing of the suitors, and the story ends happily. Over time, the word "mentor" would come to mean a wise, trusted advisor who provides counsel to those seeking success.

It's only fitting that we discuss the concept of mentorship today, on the birthday of Helen Keller, the inspirational author and social activist who taught us that one's personal deficiencies and physical disabilities are not what define us—rather it is what we accomplish even with debilitating handicaps that determines our ultimate success in life. Yet, Helen Keller's success is not just her own. She would not have become the person she was without the dedicated support of her faithful mentor, Anne Sullivan. As a trusted teacher, confidante, and eventual life-long friend, Anne gave Helen the confidence and courage to succeed.

Let's get to know the story in a bit more detail, as Helen Keller and her relationship with Anne Sullivan is one of the most inspirational examples of the three Ps to mentorship—patience, perseverance, and progress.

Born June 27, 1880, in the rural Alabama town of Tuscumbia, Helen Keller was a normal child, learning to speak at the age of six months and to walk at the age of one year. However, when Helen was 19 months old, she contracted a catastrophic infection, called brain fever, that would change her life forever. Many have debated the etiology of the infection that inflicted Helen (some claim rheumatic fever, while others assume rubella or an aggressive form of viral meningitis). Irrespective of the underlying cause, the mysterious malady would render Helen permanently blind and deaf. Over the next five years, the young girl struggled to communicate with her family, all the while growing increasingly frustrated and defiant. As her temper tantrums intensified, her exasperated family turned to a renowned specialist in Baltimore, Dr. J. Julian Chisolm, for support. Chisolm directed the family to Alexander Graham Bell. The inventor of the telephone was renowned for fitting deaf children with auditory devices to ameliorate their hearing loss. However, Helen's condition was far too complex, so Bell subsequently directed the Keller family to experts in Boston at the Perkins Institute for the Blind. The staff there recommended that Helen be paired with one of their recent graduates, Anne Sullivan, who had suffered some partial loss of her own eyesight as a child. In 1887 Anne returned to Alabama with the Keller family, where she began to teach Helen the technique of finger spelling. Using this approach, Anne would repeatedly place an object in one of Helen's hands (for example, a doll), and then spell out the corresponding word ("D-O-L-L") in Helen's other hand. The recalcitrant Helen was initially resistant to Anne's teaching style, and she failed to connect that the letters she was having spelled in one hand referred to the object in her other hand. However, one day, Helen had a watershed moment. She was able to connect the cool, flowing liquid being poured on her one hand with the word "W-A-T-E-R" being spelled in the other hand. At that moment, the concept that every word carries its own meaning was formed in her mind. In fact, by the end of that same day, Helen had voraciously learned the meaning of 30 different words.

Helen's insatiable thirst for knowledge was awakened, and her teacher Anne continued to satisfy this urge. By the age of 10, Helen had advanced enough that she was taking speech classes at the Horace

Mann School for the Deaf in Boston. From there, Helen advanced in her academic studies and her communication skills by attending increasingly more challenging schools for deaf and blind children, first in New York and then in Boston. All the while, Anne attended classes with Helen, helping interpret classroom instructions, lessons, or other text. At the age of 20, Helen was admitted to the Radcliffe College of Harvard University, where she attended classes with Anne at her side for the next four years. Her tuition was paid for by two admirers: the author Mark Twain and his wealthy friend, Standard Oil executive Henry H. Rodgers. Both men were inspired by Helen's personal progress in the face of adversity. While in college, Helen improved her speaking skills and mastered touch-sign language, touch-lip reading, Braille, and typing. At the age of 21, she published *The Story of My Life,* an autobiography of her traumatic past and her steady road to education. Helen's inspiring story was an instant success, and her national prestige grew. After college, Helen continued to reside with Anne and Anne's new husband, John Macy, an instructor Anne met while attending classes with Helen.

Now, the story could end there, and we'd all be amazed by what Helen had accomplished by graduating cum laude from Harvard. However, Helen's story was just getting started. After graduating from Harvard, Helen became an author, a social activist, and a philanthropist. She testified in front of the United States Congress to promote improved welfare of individuals with disabilities, visited and assisted wounded soldiers after both World Wars, and co-founded several organizations, including the American Civil Liberties Union (ACLU). She was an active supporter of several organizations, including the American Federation for the Blind, the American Foundation for Overseas Blind, and the Helen Keller International; the latter one was specifically dedicated to research for blindness and healthy nutrition. She advocated publicly against war and violence, campaigned for women's suffrage, and lectured against child labor practices. All the while, Anne was always by her side until her own death in 1936.

Having lost her trusted mentor and best friend, Helen turned to another colleague, Polly Thompson, who stepped in to fill the void left by Anne. Together, Helen and Polly partnered on numerous goodwill missions—many focused on improving international care for those with physical disabilities. Although some contemporaries argued that Helen's socialist views were a bit extreme, most marveled at her tremendous accomplishments and gladly welcomed her visits. She and

Polly travelled extensively to over 40 countries, where they advocated for the rights of the blind and disabled patients. Her efforts led to many nations enacting laws and policies to improve the conditions for the blind, the deaf, and those with other physical or mental disabilities. When President Dwight D. Eisenhower strove to improve US/Japan relations after the devastation of World War II, he turned to Helen as his special envoy to visit Japan. She was welcomed in Tokyo and other Japanese cities, thereby helping to build a bridge between the two adversarial nations. By the time Helen Keller died at the age of 88, her steadfast determination, empathic approach, and kind spirit had changed the world.

Of course, none of this would have happened without the commitment, loyalty, and staunch support of her mentor—Anne Sullivan. Anne taught Helen that progress is always possible if one approaches life's hindrances with a little patience and a lot of perseverance. Again, we return to the three Ps of mentoring: patience, perseverance, and progress.

However, I don't want to leave you thinking that someone must have a handicap to seek the guidance and enlightenment of a mentor. Some of the greatest personal success stories the world has known involve the support of a mentor. In prior segments, I've told how Socrates served as a mentor to many aspiring youth in ancient Greece, including his best known pupil, Plato. Plato would pay it forward by sharing his philosophy, knowledge, and wisdom with those who attended his higher institution of learning, The Academy; one of Plato's own students, Aristotle, would form his own institution, The Lyceum, where he would also assume a mentorship role. But, did you know that the American transcendentalist philosopher and author of *Walden* and *Civil Disobedience*, Henry David Thoreau, was mentored for many years by the great American author Ralph Waldo Emerson? Or that the awe-inspiring leader Martin Luther King Jr. relied heavily on the guidance and mentorship of his Morehouse College professor Benjamin Elijah Mays? Or that the TV celebrity Oprah Winfrey called on the American poet and civil rights leader Maya Angelou on many occasions to help her through times of need? Or that the technocrat Steve Jobs paid it forward by serving as a confidante to Facebook's founder Mark Zuckerberg, just as he was starting out in the fast-paced world of Silicon Valley? I was even pleasantly surprised to hear that our own CEO, Ken Frazier, still turns to his friend and mentor, Dr. P. Roy

Vagelos (the former Merck Research Laboratories Head turned Merck CEO), in times of need (**Figure 25**).

We all can benefit from a mentor.

In my career, I have been blessed to have some incredible mentors. I can recall how an infectious disease specialist and the Dean of Students at Emory University School of Medicine, Jonas (Jack) Shulman, was routinely there for me when I was a bumbling medical student. He encouraged me to apply for an internship in Internal Medicine at Massachusetts General Hospital, even when I was not thoroughly convinced I would make the grade. Jack's enthusiastic love of infectious diseases helped instill in me a similar affection and appreciation for this incredible discipline. In past segments, I've told how folks like Morton Swartz and Carole Sable not only mentored me in my early career, but also inspired me to strive to be better as a physician, a clinical trialist, and a team leader. More recently, I've looked to numerous folks within the Merck organization who've given me scholarly guidance on how to be a more strategic thinker, a more engaging presenter, and an inspirational leader. In the past, I've turned to a career coach outside of Merck who has helped me piece together what I really want my role as a leader within the Merck organization to be. I'm also blessed to have family members, such as my spouse Daisy and my older brother Phil, who've guided me along the way and have even walked me off an emotional cliff or two.

I recently read a fascinating article on the internet from an Inc. com blogger, Glenn Leibowitz, in which he reflects on what constitutes a great mentor. In his estimation, what separates an ordinary teacher from a true mentor is the following: Mentors care enough to share their wisdom to help guide someone along a personal or professional journey. Much like the elder Mentor did for Telemachus, a great mentor can be a problem-solving partner that affords his/her mentee some direction but still leaves it up to that individual mentee to find their own path. A great mentor challenges you to think beyond your assumptions, but he/she does not tell you what to think. A great mentor also encourages you to try something different or outside the box, providing you the encouragement, confidence, and optimism to help you reach beyond your traditional limits or perceived boundaries. In other words, a great mentor gives you the courage to take personal action, even when you are equivocating or showing trepidation. A great mentor is a truth teller; he/she should not shy away from telling you the way something is—even if you don't want to hear it.

So, today I'm thankful to all those individuals who have taken the time to serve as mentors for me. In my own career odyssey, I've relied on many of my friends, family, and work colleagues to help me persevere in life. These trusted compatriots have been there to provide a differing perspective, shine a light on a pressing issue, or help me solve a personal conundrum. In turn, I'm trying to pay it forward by serving as a mentor to several of my own coworkers who've asked for my guidance. As your schedule allows, I'd encourage you and other leaders to follow suit by serving as mentors to those seeking your guidance. Frankly, mentorship is one of the most rewarding roles I've ever undertaken in my career.

Let's be honest. We always think others are wiser than we are. But the truth of the matter is that there is nothing magical about wisdom. Nobody wakes up one morning and is suddenly blessed with the wisdom of a gifted seer. Wisdom is really just the culmination of learnings from our prior experiences, including our foibles, missteps, and wrongdoings. Most of the time, all I'm doing when I'm mentoring someone is to provide empathetic, practical advice on what has and has not personally worked for me in the past. Basically, I'm just trying to make sure a mentee doesn't step into the same morass of crap I've stepped in.

All of this brings me back to Homer.

One of the great gifts that Homer and the other Greek authors left to humanity is an acknowledgement of our own fallibility. According to the ancient Greeks, the greatest of all the fatal flaws is *hubris*, maintaining a foolish sense of pride or dangerous overconfidence. All too often in my career as a physician I've seen individuals whose egos have become so inflated that they convince themselves that they possess all the answers and can handle a complex, multifaceted issue on their own. Sadly, many healthcare providers have been taught that they need to be strong by persevering on their own. But the simple truth of the matter is that the greatest sin a caregiver can commit is to let his/her pride get in the way of the care of another. Frankly, the same reality applies to all of us.

Our journey in life, whether at home or at work, is arduous, complicated, and, at times, seemingly impossible. No one expects you to have all the answers. In fact, no one expects you to do it alone. Helen Keller didn't do it on her own. Neither did Plato. Nor did Aristotle, Henry David Thoreau, Martin Luther King Jr., Oprah Winfrey, or Mark Zuckerberg.

What makes you think you must brave it on your own?

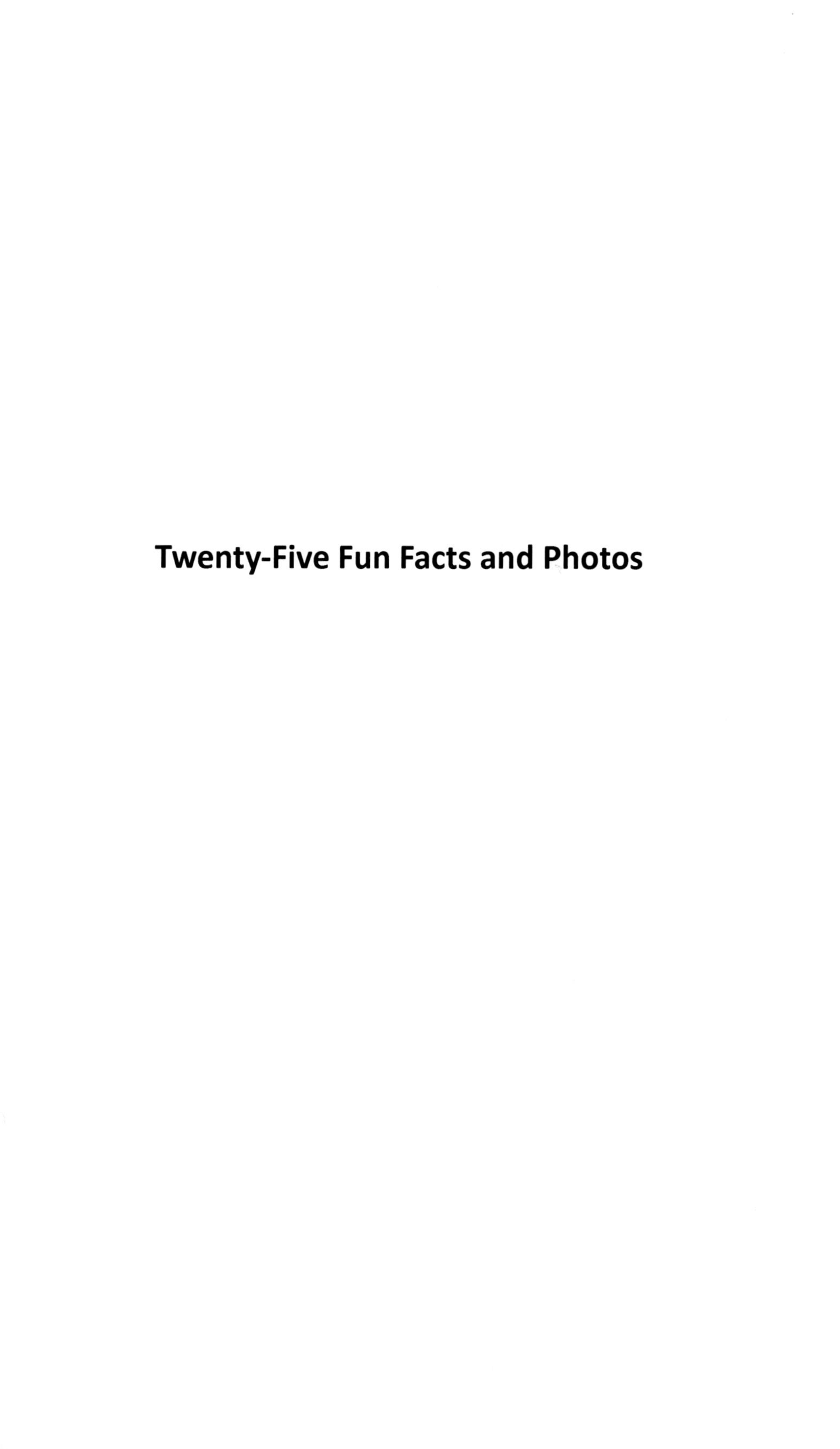

Twenty-Five Fun Facts and Photos

Figure 1. A Dynamic Duo of Antibacterial Drug Discovery

Jean Kahan was a Merck researcher involved in the discovery and development of several antibacterials, including the first-of-class antibacterial agent of the carbapenem class (imipenem). Together with her husband, Fred Kahan, Jean spearheaded a team instrumental in helping bring imipenem to the market in 1985. In short, the Kahans were another dynamic duo deserving of distinction. *(Photo courtesy of The Merck Archives, Heritage Werks, Inc.)*

Figure 2. The Honorable Dr. Hilleman

Maurice Hilleman was a Merck biologist who helped develop many of the pediatric vaccines administered to children today. The world owes a debt of gratitude to this mastermind from Miles City, Montana. *(Photo courtesy of The Merck Archives, Heritage Werks, Inc.)*

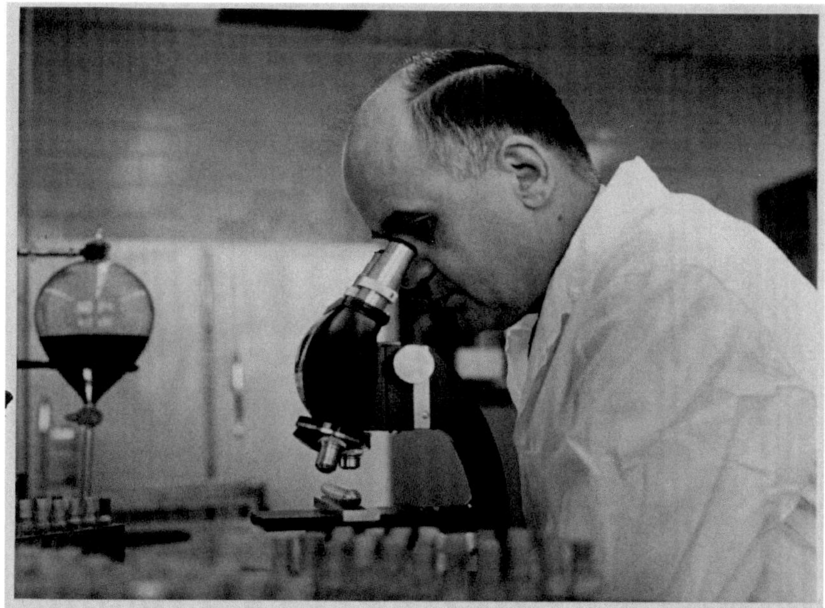

Figure 3. A Phenomenal Philanthropist Who Changed World

In the heart of Emory College's stunning campus, at the foot of the Robert W. Woodruff library, stands a larger-than-life, bronze stature honoring the library's namesake. As the former CEO of Coca-Cola, Inc. and Emory's preeminent philanthropist, Mr. Woodruff was a larger-than-life figure. Hence, it is only fitting that Emory's main library, affectionately known as "The Stacks," is dedicated to a man that has afforded many youths the opportunity to attend such an esteemed university as Emory. *(Photo courtesy of the author).*

Figure 4. Hungry Dogs Run Fast!

At Lincoln Financial Field, the home of the Philadelphia Eagles, a stone entryway has been created wherein fanatic fans can express their unfeigned support of their beloved "Iggles." Can you find the etched stone that depicts the Kartsonis' adoration for the team? Notice how all family members are acknowledged, even our trusted dog, Jango! Jason Kelce would be so proud. *(Photo courtesy of the author).*

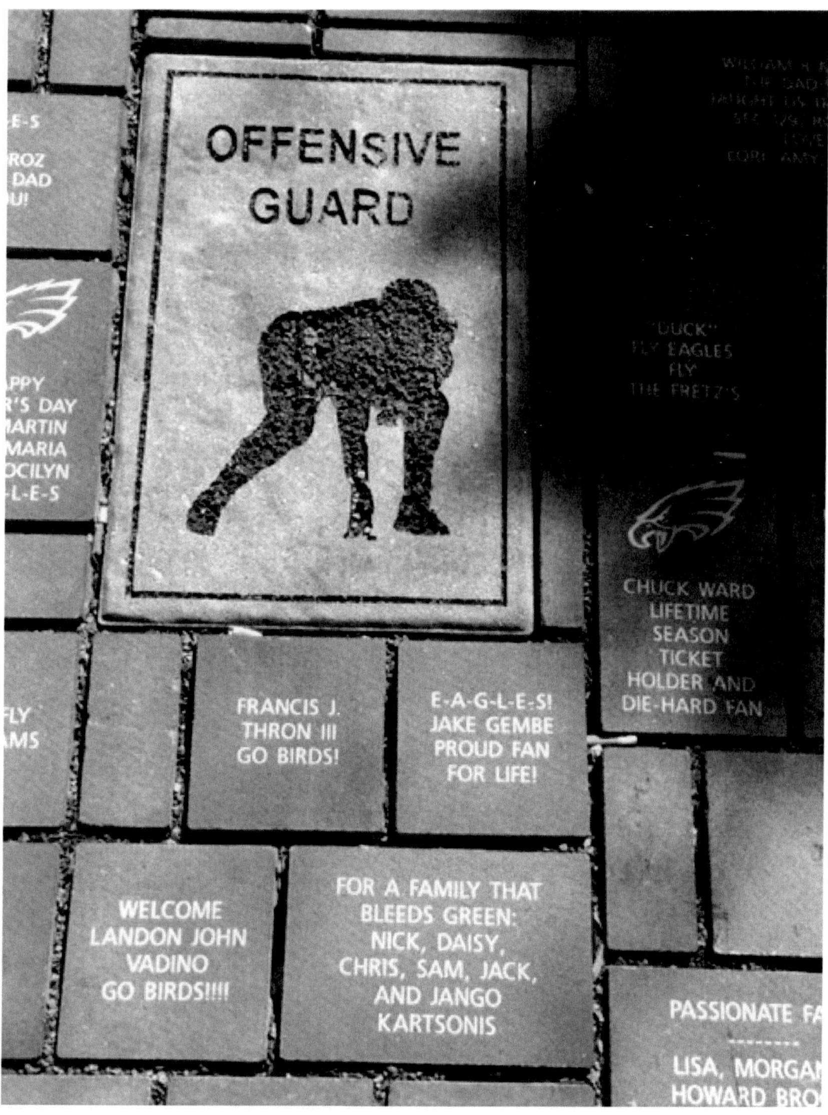

Figure 5. You Want Philly Philly?

The stupendous achievement of a 2018 Super Bowl championship win for the City of Brotherly Love was commemorated with a bronze statue that sits within the atrium of Lincoln Financial Field, the home of the Philadelphia Eagles. The statue depicts the huddle between quarterback Nick Foles and Coach Doug Pederson that led to the most ingenious and courageous play call in the history of the National Football League. By the way, Coach Pederson's response to Foles's query was sheer perfection: "Yeah, let's do it." My youngest son, Jack, and I share a moment together prior to a 2018 game. *(Photo courtesy of the author).*

Figure 6. The MECTIZAN® Mission

The Merck decision in 1987 to supply ivermectin (MECTIZAN®) to those regions of the world inflicted with the parasite that causes river blindness was a crowning achievement of Dr. P. Roy Vagelos's era as Merck CEO. In this picture, Dr. Vagelos is depicted with Former President Jimmy Carter and First Lady Rosalynn Carter on a visit to a village in Chad, Africa. *(Photo courtesy of The Merck Archives, Heritage Werks, Inc.)*

Figure 7. Socrates' Solemn Site of Sacrifice

In Athens, Greece, just a stone's throw from the Acropolis and the Ancient Agora (marketplace), there lies a rock enclosure that reportedly served as the prison for the great Greek philosopher Socrates. Located on Philoppapos Hill, the jail site is not a heavily-visited tourist destination. Nevertheless, it is an attraction I always visit when I go to Greece, for it serves as a poignant reminder of how sometimes we punish those who should otherwise be praised. *(Photo courtesy of the author).*

Figure 8. The Electric Connection between Thomas Edison & Merck

In addition to serving as a mentor and neighbor to George W. Merck, the Wizard of Menlo Park also collaborated with researchers at Merck. The following contract drawn up by Thomas Alva Edison himself is a wonderful glimpse into how business deals were conducted nearly a century ago. *(Photo courtesy of The Merck Archives, Heritage Werks, Inc.)*

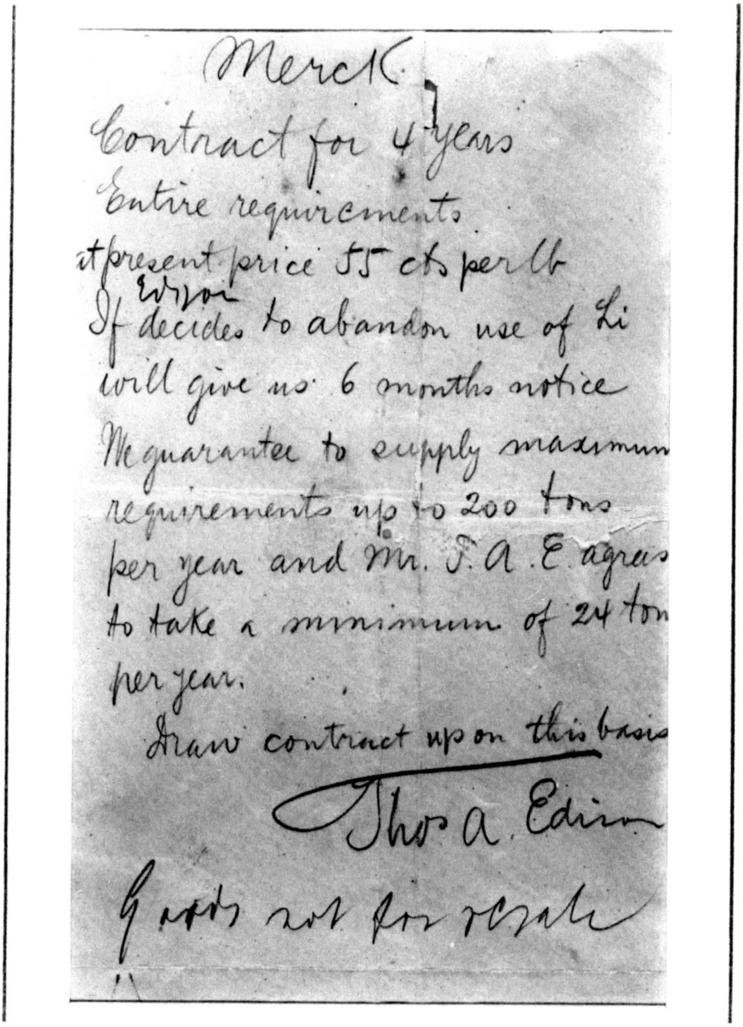

Merck
Contract for 4 years
Entire requirements
at present price 55 cts per lb
If Edison decides to abandon use of Li
will give us 6 months notice
We guarantee to supply maximum
requirements up to 200 tons
per year and Mr. T. A. E. agrees
to take a minimum of 24 tons
per year.
Draw contract up on this basis
Thos A. Edison
Goods not for resale

Figure 9. Riveting Research in Rahway

Although Merck occupied the Rahway site just a few miles south of Newark in 1903, the New Jersey site did not become a bona fide research facility until the 1930s. Below are two pictures from within the Merck research library and research laboratory, circa 1935. *(Photo courtesy of The Merck Archives, Heritage Werks, Inc.)*

Figure 10. In the Presence of Nobility

In this now-famous photograph, the scientists who discovered streptomycin (Selman Waksman, left) and penicillin (Sir Alexander Fleming, right) are seated at a table populated with petri dishes, as the Merck chemist and first head of the Merck research facility, Randolph Major, looks on. Both Fleming and Waksman won the Nobel Prize for Physiology or Medicine for their respective discoveries. *(Photo courtesy of The Merck Archives, Heritage Werks, Inc.)*

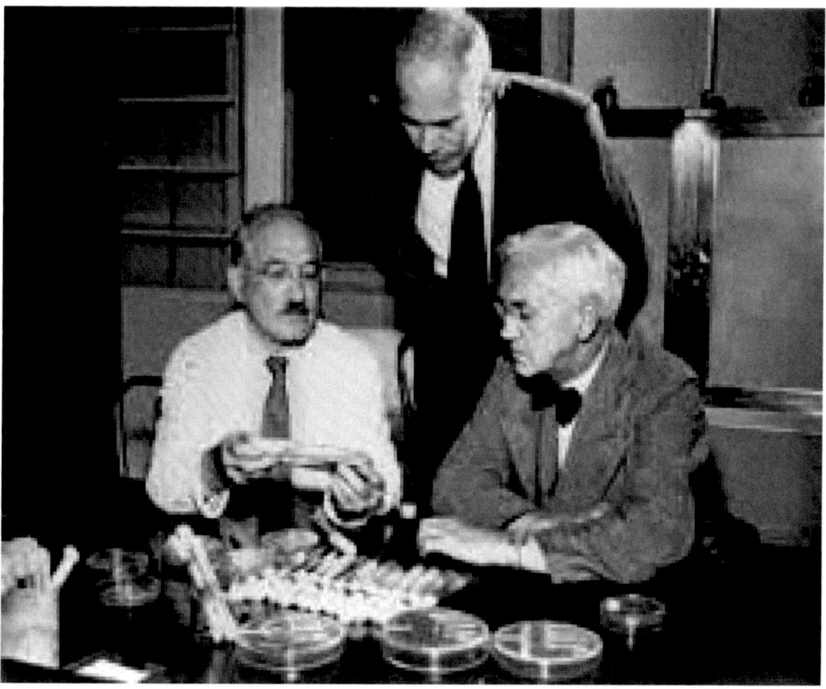

Figure 11. The March to End Polio

Prior to its elimination from the Americas, polio was one of several viral diseases for which Merck developed a vaccine. In particular, Merck was instrumental in the manufacture of the Salk inactivated polio vaccine. A photo of one of the early vials produced at the West Point site in Pennsylvania is shown below. *(Photo courtesy of The Merck Archives, Heritage Werks, Inc.)*

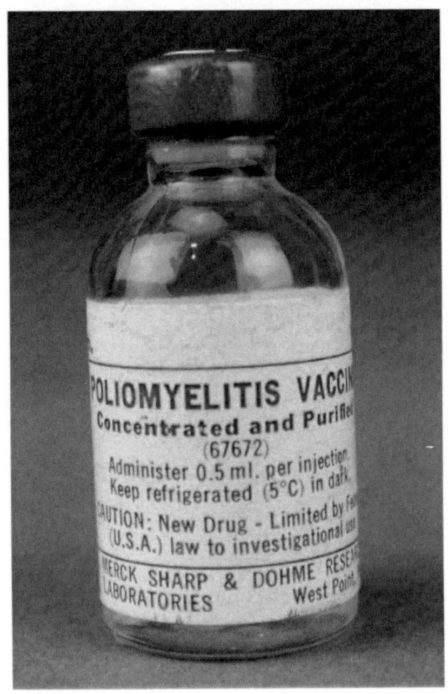

Figure 12. Jango!

Our 10 year-old golden retriever, Jango, is a beloved member of the Kartsonis household. In this photo, he sits regally in our master bedroom, blending into the rug. Technically, he is not allowed in our bedroom, but those rules are not fully enforced whenever my spouse, Daisy, chooses to work from home. Incidentally, this never happens when I work from home. *(Photo courtesy of Cynthia D. Smith)*

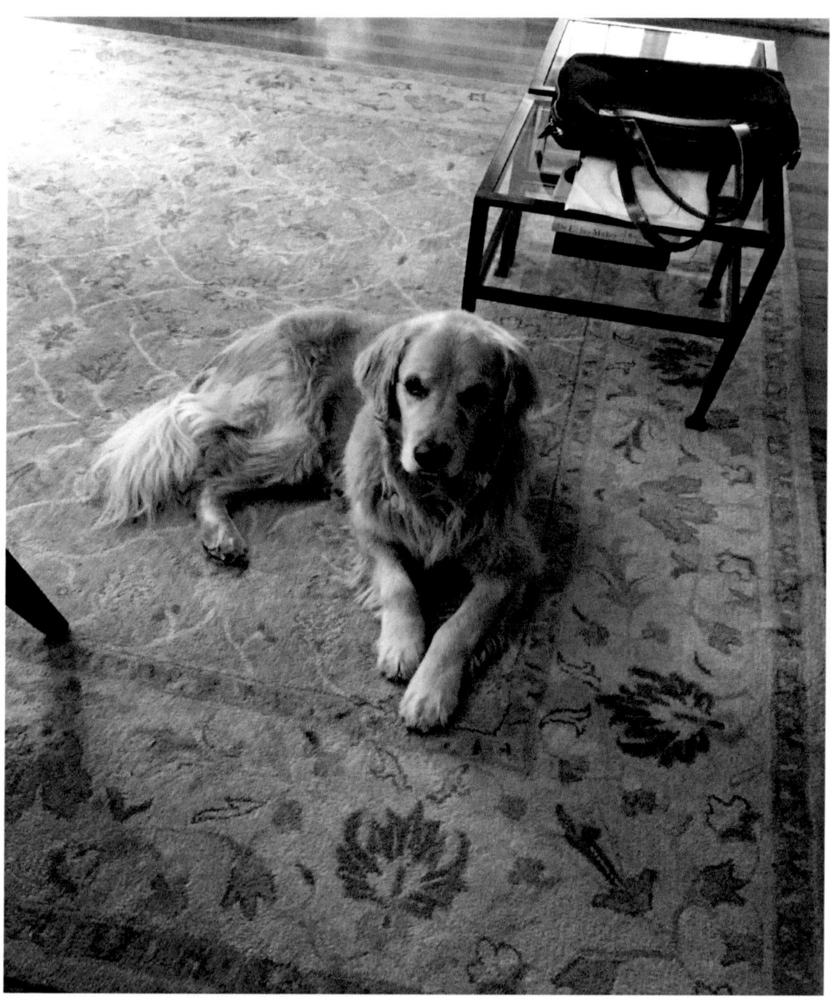

Figure 13. A Healthy Chicken in Every Pot

The first product that heralded the birth of Merck Animal Health was targeted to address coccidiosis, a devastating parasitic infection in poultry. Licensed in 1948, sulfaquinoxaline (SQ®, for short) helped transform the poultry industry. The following ad, published in 1951, highlighted the incredible shielding attributes of this novel product. *(Photo courtesy of The Merck Archives, Heritage Werks, Inc.)*

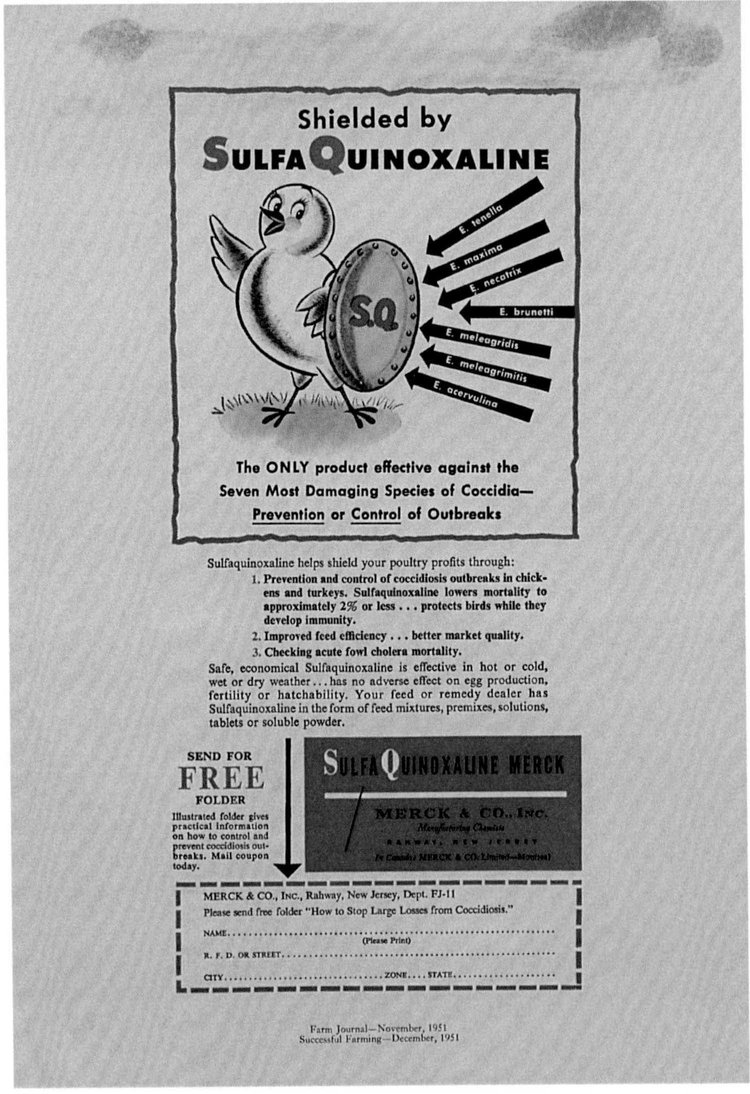

Figure 14. Getting Vaccinated by a Legend

Dr. Jonas Salk, the vaccinologist responsible for the development of the polio vaccine, actively participated in the institution of the now-famous Francis Field Trial. In this photo, Dr. Salk is administering the vaccine to a brave trial participant. *(Photo courtesy of The Merck Archives, Heritage Werks, Inc.)*

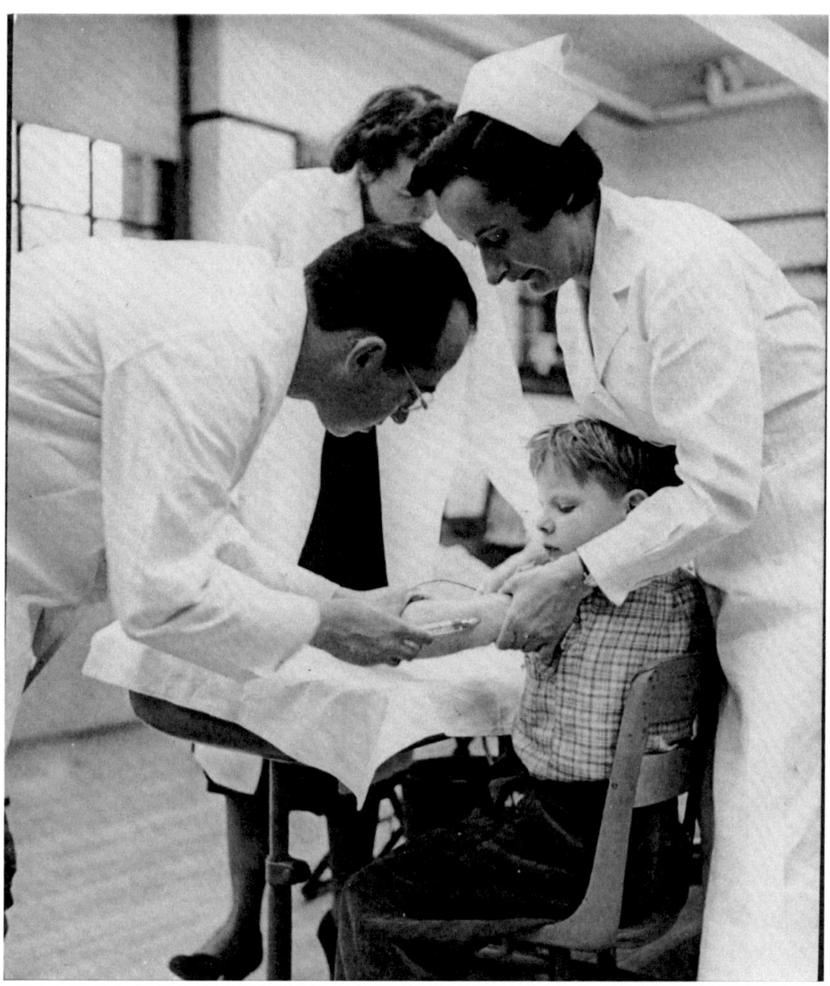

Figure 15. The Bold Birth of Biologics

In 1895, the Philadelphia-based pharmaceutical company H.K. Mulford Pharmaceuticals introduced to the market the first of many antisera compounds, an antitoxin targeting the dangerous bacterium *Clostridium diphtheriae.* This illustrated advertisement from the early 20th century highlights the protective, almost angelic value of antisera against these deadly bacterial pathogens. *(Photo courtesy of The Merck Archives, Heritage Werks, Inc.)*

Figure 16. The Lasting Legacy of Latrodectus: Black Widow Spider Antivenom

The only remaining antiserum manufactured by Merck is the antivenom against the bite of *Latrodectus mactans*, the dreaded female black willow spider. Merck continues to serve as the sole provider of this antivenom, which is still generated to this day with the assistance of Pennsylvania-based horses. *(Photo courtesy of The Merck Archives, Heritage Werks, Inc.)*

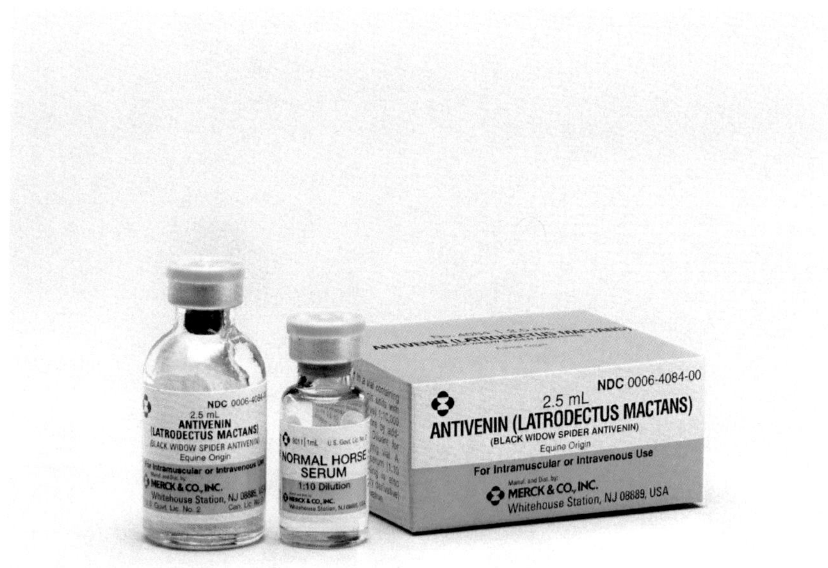

Figure 17. A Game Changer

Between 1987 and 1996, Merck discovered, developed, and manufactured the protease inhibitor indinavir sulfate. In combination with two other anti-HIV medications, indinavir sulfate helped transform the treatment of people living with HIV infection, essentially transforming the disease from a death sentence to a chronic infection. Shown below is a photo from the mid-1990s of a Merck Manufacturing Division employee supervising the packaging of indinavir sulfate. *(Photo courtesy of The Merck Archives, Heritage Werks, Inc.)*

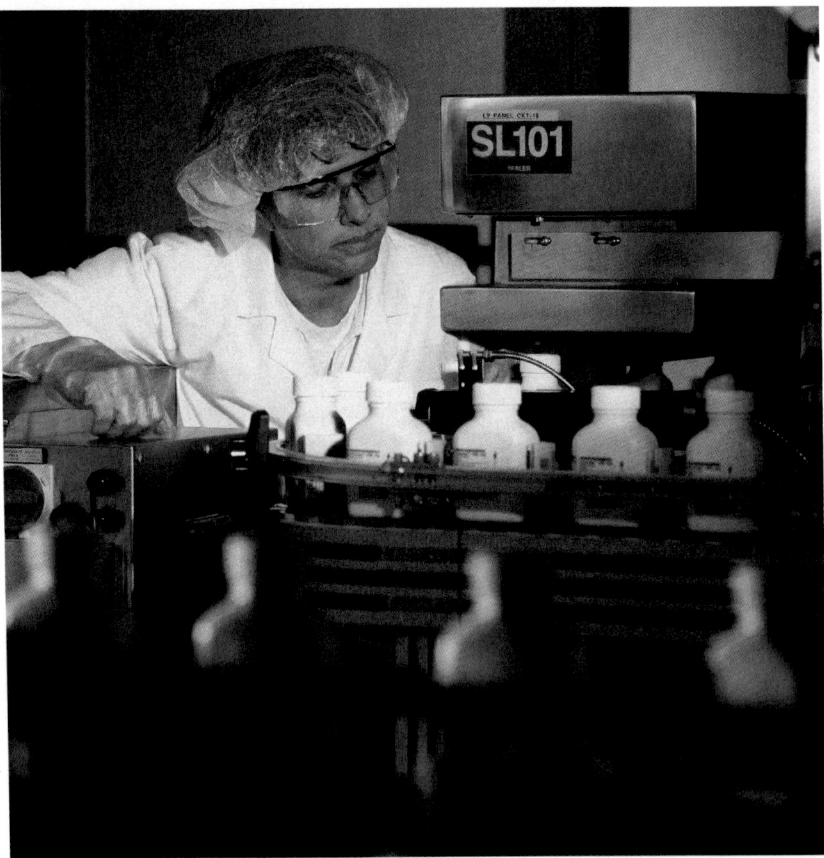

Figure 18. Merck's Founding Father

In 1891, George F. Merck came to the United States to lead the US division of the German-based pharmaceutical company, E. Merck AG. In 1917, with America's entry into World War I, George readily complied with the US government mandate to sever his Company's ties with the German parent, and Merck & Co., Inc. was born. You gotta love the handlebar moustache! *(Photo courtesy of The Merck Archives, Heritage Werks, Inc.)*

Figure 19. A Picture to Make Any Papa Proud

George F. Merck gained his US citizenship and started a family in Llewellyn Park, a rolling hill suburb of West Orange, with his wife, Friedrike. George and Friedrike had 5 children, including their oldest, George W. Merck, who was born in 1894 and is shown below with the proud father in this grainy photo. *(Photo courtesy of The Merck Archives, Heritage Werks, Inc.)*

Figure 20. The Inauguration of Pharmaceutical-Based Research

In 1933, George W. Merck, the son of George F. Merck and the second individual to lead Merck & Co., Inc., established Merck's Research & Development division—a novel concept for the time. Taking a lesson from Edison, George W. created a university-like laboratory atmosphere to help attract research talent from local academic powerhouses. George W. Merck also wanted the Research and Development division to operate like a university lab. Scientists would be allowed to pursue research regardless of practical gains and publish their research in academic journals, a practice that was unheard of at the time as most pharmaceutical companies considered their research results to be a trade secret. The announcement of the division was heralded with a celebration at the Rahway campus, at the site of the eventual building. In the distance, one can appreciate what a traffic jam looked like in 1933. *(Photo courtesy of The Merck Archives, Heritage Werks, Inc.)*

Figure 21. Providing Penicillin for the Platoons

After George W. Merck agreed to support penicillin production for the World War II effort in December 1941, the Merck pilot plant in Rahway produced several hundred liters of penicillin. By March 1942, Merck had generated enough penicillin to treat the first patient in New Haven, Connecticut. Over the next few years, various steps in the manufacturing process were significantly enhanced. The vintage poster, which was used to help promote Merck's involvement in the war effort, also provides a bird's eye view of Merck's iconic Rahway facility. The smoke stack with the Merck emblem still stands to this day. *(Photo courtesy of The Merck Archives, Heritage Werks, Inc.)*

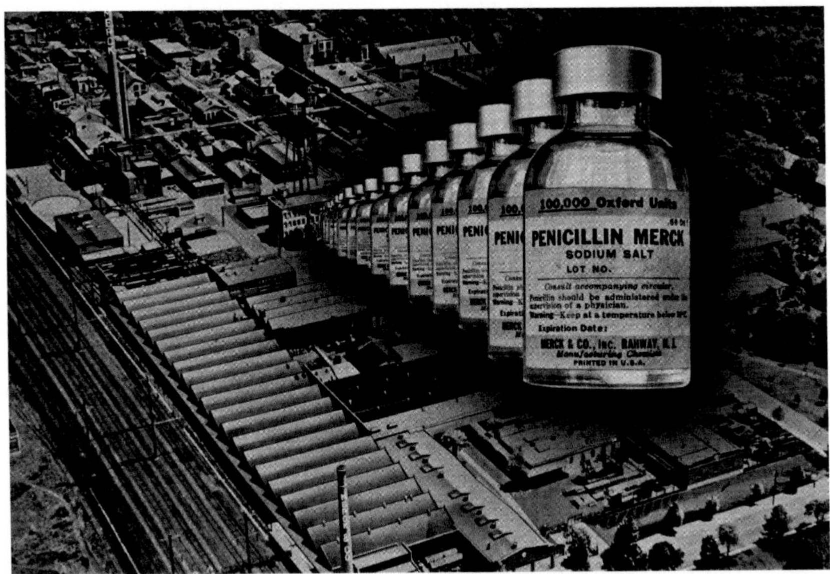

Figure 22. Plentiful Packaging of Penicillin for the Patients

In 1943 alone, Merck produced 4.18 billion units of penicillin. Shown here are several Merck workers packing crates of penicillin to be shipped via railway during the war-time effort. It looks like back-breaking work. *(Photo courtesy of The Merck Archives, Heritage Werks, Inc.)*

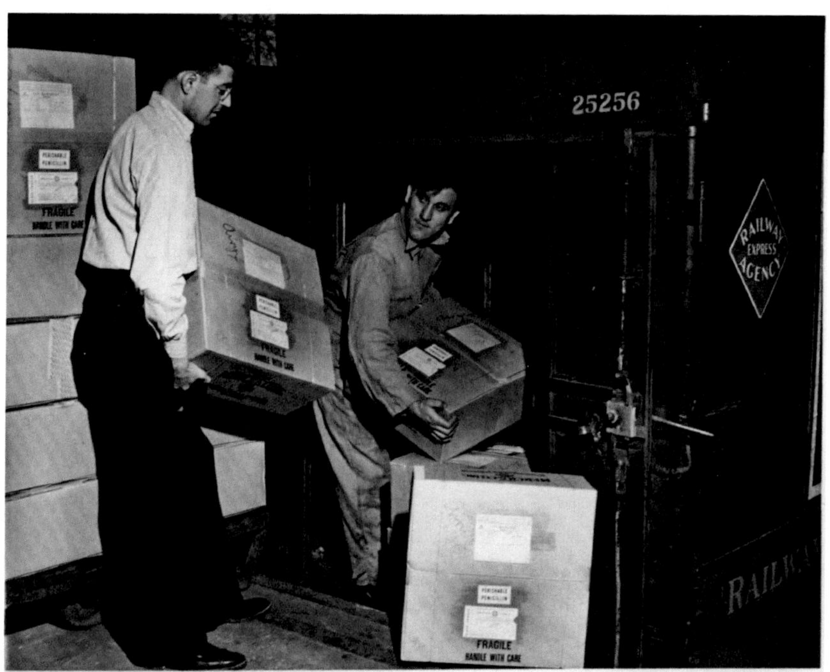

Figure 23. A Magnum Opus of Medical Knowledge

The first edition of the *Merck Manual of the Materia Medica* was published in 1899. Divided into three easily navigated parts, this 192-page pocket-sized guide sold for just one dollar. A photo of an original edition of The Manual illustrates how this paper-bound guide could fit snugly into the healthcare provider's pocket. (Photo courtesy of The Merck Archives, Heritage Werks, Inc.)

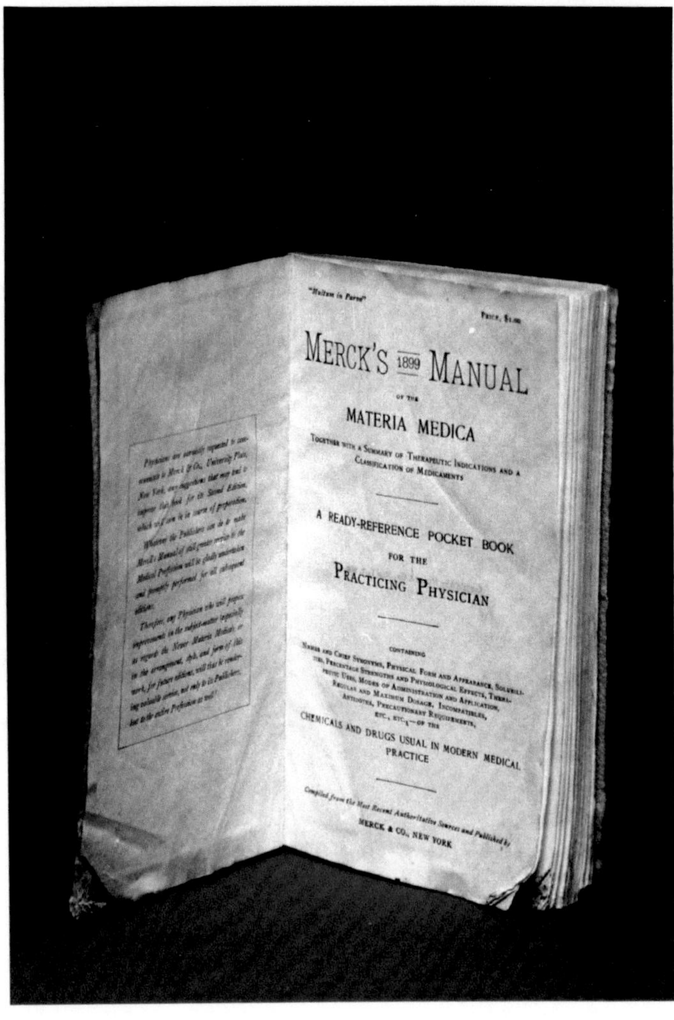

Figure 24. The Magnification of the Merck Manual

By 1942, the size of *The Merck Manual* had ballooned to 1,496 pages, but the price had only marginally increased to $2. Shipping and handling outside of the US came at an additional cost; nevertheless, what a bargain! The latest edition, the twentieth edition, is a whopping 3,584 pages and weighs 6 pounds. *(Photo courtesy of The Merck Archives, Heritage Werks, Inc.)*

Figure 25. Mentorship at Merck

Over the last few decades, P. Roy Vagelos (right) has served as a mentor to Merck's current CEO, Kenneth Frazier (left). Their mutual respect and admiration is evident in this photo from an event celebrating the 25th anniversary of the initiation of the MECTIZAN® donation program. *(Photo courtesy of The Merck Archives, Heritage Werks, Inc.)*

Acknowledgments

I'd like to close by taking a moment to acknowledge several incredible individuals who've helped in the creation of this book.

First and foremost, I need to take a moment to thank all the former and current employees who've worked at Merck and have made this company into the success it is today. Many of my essays tell the compelling story of a corporate icon, Merck & Co., Inc. Some of the predecessors who changed the world as Merck employees are already chronicled in this various stories I relay in this book. Nevertheless, I'd like to take a moment to express my gratefulness to many of my current and former Merck scientific colleagues, including Jeff Chodakewitz, Carole Sable, Robin Isaacs, Eliav Barr, Joan Butterton, Paula Annunziato, George Hanna, Deb Fisher, Leigh Shultz, Jen McClellan, Susan Ajalat, Roy Baynes, Roger Perlmutter, and Ken Frazier, who've served as my role models, coaches, friends, and mentors. You and so many others I've not listed here are all an endless source of inspiration to me.

I also want to acknowledge my wonderful editor, Deborah Lange, and my astute publisher, Audrey Wolf, for helping me transform my stories into this final version. Their vision, input, and support has greatly improved the book. I am grateful for them being such an enormously valuable resource. I'm also extremely appreciative to my colleagues at The Merck Archives, Heritage Werks Inc. In particular, I want to thank Julie Renner and Chelsey Cain for all their support in identifying and providing relevant photos and artifacts from their vast vault of archives.

Next, I'm endlessly indebted to my wonderful wife, Daisy, for having to listen to me drone on for nearly a year about *Thankful Thursdays.* I've talked her ears off about my quirky ideas, historical references, and the book's (seemingly never-ending) composition. I've taken up too much of your precious time on way too many of our weekend, early-morning walks. All the while, you've faithfully listened, smiled, and offered your sage advice. I am so deeply grateful for your partnership, and I'm blessed to have you and our three wonderful offspring in my life.

Speaking of our trio of children, I need to send a hearty shout-out to my incredibly awesome sons – Chris, Sam, and Jack. I admire, love, and respect you dearly. You are all maturing into intelligent, hard-working, and, most importantly, kind men. Daisy would also insist that I mention the word "feminist" here. Although I'm not sure any of you will take the time to read this book in its entirety (that is, I recognize it is a bit longer than a text), you are all so worthy of my praise for what fine gentlemen you have become.

Finally, I'm indebted to my many colleagues at Merck & Co., Inc., who graciously served as my Thursday morning readers, cheerleaders, and critics. As my imprisoned readers of these weekly blogs, you've been my willing study participants in this somewhat unorthodox clinical experiment. Along this year-long trial, we've embarked on a wild journey together. I've been humbled and struck by how many of you have encouraged me with your insightful ideas, objective candidness, and profound kindness. So, for one last time, let me say, "Thank you for being such a wonderful set of willing colleagues." Time will only tell what future initiative I'm apt to unjustly subject you to. I offer my sincere thanks and apologies in advance.